KU-329-317

[Moin L.3]

LOGO MATHEMATICS IN THE CLASSROOM

The use of computers in the classroom has brought with it new challenges, ideas and ways of thinking and has revitalised the education debate. It has generated enthusiasm and a new involvement in learning from pupils, teachers and parents alike. In particular, the upsurge in the use of Logo is seen by the authors of this book as a way of providing opportunities for mathematical investigation, encouraging discussion and project work, and making mathematics more open and practical, accessible and popular to a greater number of pupils.

Logo Mathematics in the Classroom explores a wide range of issues within mathematics education. It draws from the experience of three-year, longitudinal, classroom-based study of pairs of secondary school children who used Logo as part of their mathematics curriculum. The authors describe in detail the processes of learning Logo and the mathematical activities involved. They use data from the study to identify misconceptions and gender differences, and make suggestions for new approaches to classroom practice.

Dr Celia Hoyles is a Professor of Mathematics Education and **Dr Rosamund Sutherland** is a research lecturer, both at the Institute of Education, University of London. They jointly directed the Logo Maths Project (1983–6), and since 1986 have continued researching with children and with teachers using a variety of software and focusing on a range of mathematical ideas.

LOGO MATHEMATICS IN THE CLASSROOM

CELIA HOYLES AND ROSAMUND SUTHERLAND

London and New York

First published 1989
by Routledge
11 New Fetter Lane, London EC4P 4EE
29 West 35th Street, New York, NY 10001

New in paperback 1992

© 1989 Celia Hoyles and Rosamund Sutherland

Typeset by LaserScript Ltd, Mitcham, Surrey
Printed and bound in Great Britain by
Mackays of Chatham PLC, Chatham, Kent

All rights reserved. No part of this book may be
reprinted or reproduced or utilised in any form or
by any electronic, mechanical, or other means, now
known or hereafter invented, including photocopying
and recording, or in any information storage or
retrieval system, without permission in writing from
the publishers.

British Library Cataloguing in Publication Data

A catalogue record
for this book is available
from the British Library
ISBN 0–415–07791–0

Library of Congress Cataloging in Publication Data

Has been applied for
ISBN 0–415–0779–0

Contents

List of Figures   vi
List of Tables   ix
Acknowledgements   x

1   General Introduction   1
2   The Logo Maths Project   5
3   Selected Logo Projects   16
4   Problem Solving   55
5   Subprocedure and Modularity   70
6   Some Common Pupil Misconceptions about Logo
    Programming   89
7   Pupils Collaborating in a Programming Environment   97
8   Turtle Turn and Angle   116
9   The Teacher's Role   140
10 Gender Issues   159
11 Pupils' Intuitive Mathematical Conceptions   178
12 Understanding Algebraic Ideas   194
13 Conclusions   219
    Appendix 1. Overview of Logo Commands   226
    Appendix 2. Categories of Pupil Discourse   228
    References   230
    Index   234

List of Figures

2.1	The Letter F	6
2.2	Beginning Logo Handout	11
3.1	STAR	18
3.2	SS, Superstar	18
3.3	FS, Forward Star	19
3.4	SFS, Super Forward Star (First Attempt)	19
3.5	SFS, Super Forward Star (Second Attempt)	19
3.6	FS (Modified)	20
3.7	SDS, Superduperstar	20
3.8	SDDS	21
3.9	SDDDS	21
3.10	A Row of Stars	22
3.11	STARBUSTER	23
3.12	The 'Circular Spiral' Task	26
3.13	A First Attempt	26
3.14	A Second Attempt	27
3.15	A Third Attempt	27
3.16	Extending the Spiral	28
3.17	General Right Hand Spiral (First Attempt)	30
3.18	General Right Hand Spiral (Second Attempt)	31
3.19	A Spiral Pattern	32
3.20	Building up Spiral Patterns	32
3.21	First Attempt at a Cube	36
3.22	First Attempt at a Cuboid	36
3.23	Second Attempt at a Cuboid	37
3.24	The Cube Revisited	38
3.25	Final Attempt at a Cube	38
3.26	An Aeroplane	41
3.27	An Aeroplane, Part 1	44
3.28	An Aeroplane, Part 2	45
3.29	The Completed Aeroplane	47
3.30	A Square Procedure	48
3.31	A Closed Shape	51
4.1	George and Asim: The Butterfly	60
4.2	Sally and Janet: The Prison	61
4.3	Classification of Pupil Goals	63

4.4	Type of Programming Activity	65
4.5	Sally and Janet: The Butterfly	68
5.1	Example of 'Top-down' Design	70
5.2	The House	74
5.3	Rotated Pattern of Squares	75
5.4	The Rabbit	76
5.5	The Star	77
5.6	The 'Row of Pines' Task	78
5.7	The 'Four Squares' Task	79
5.8	Year 1: Sally and George's Individual Solutions to the 'Four Squares' Task	81
5.9	Year 3: Sally and George's Individual Solutions to the 'Four Squares' Task	81
5.10	The 'Decreasing Squares' Task	82
5.11	Structure Emerging	84
5.12	No Evidence of Structure	84
6.1	The 'Four Squares' Task	91
6.2	Ravi's Solution to the 'Four Squares' Task	93
6.3	The 'Decreasing Squares' Task	95
6.4	Sally's Solution to the 'Decreasing Squares' Task	95
7.1	The 'Spiral' Task	103
7.2	Part of a Spiral	106
7.3	The 'Lollipop' Task	109
7.4	(a) Sally's 'Lollipop' Procedure	110
	(b) Janet's 'Lollipop' Procedure	110
7.5	(a) George's 'Lollipop' Procedure	110
	(b) Asim's 'Lollipop' Procedure	110
7.6	The 'Arrow' Task	111
7.7	Sally and Janet's 'Arrow' Procedure	114
8.1	George and Asim: The Face	122
8.2	Planning for a Turtle	123
8.3	First Step in Turtle Construction	124
8.4	The Turtle	126
8.5	The Goal Post	127
8.6	The 'M' Debugging Task	129
8.7	Janet's Procedure for 'M' Debugging Task	131
8.8	Janet's Attempt at the 'Puzzle' Tracing Task	132
8.9	Janet's Attempt at the 'Pat' Tracing Task	133

8.10   Janet's Attempt at the 'REPEAT' Task   134
8.11   Pupils' Interpretations of 'Input of 90'   135
8.12   Janet's Response to Request to Label 'Turn of 60' in
       a Hexagon   136
8.13   Janet's Interpretation of 'RT 45' and 'RT 135'   136

9.1   The 'SMILE' Task   148
9.2   The 'Variable Squares' Task   149
9.3   Sally and Janet's First Attempt at a Program   150
9.4   Sally and Janet's Second Attempt at a Program   151
9.5   The 'Regular Polygon' Task   152
9.6   The 'Row of Pines' Task   156

10.1   The 'K' Task   167
10.2   The 'M' Debugging Task   167
10.3   The 'Decreasing Squares' Task   168
10.4   The 'Arrow' Task   171

11.1   The 'Rotated Patterns' Task   181
11.2   Linda and Jude's Solution to the 'Row of Pines' Task   186
11.3   Mary and Nadia: Variable Star   187
11.4   The 'Arrow' Task   190

12.1   The 'Scaling Letter' Task   198
12.2   Sally and Janet: Extension of the 'Scaling Letter' Task 198
12.3   Linda and Elaine: Extension of the 'Scaling Letter'
       Task   199
12.4   Procedure with One Variable Input   201
12.5   (a)Variable as Scale Factor   202
       (b)More than One Variable Input   202
       (c)Variable Operated On   202
12.6   General Superprocedure   203
12.7   Tail Recursive Procedure   203
12.8   Function Representations   204
12.9   The 'Function Machine' Task   205
12.10 The 'Paper and Pencil Function Machine' Task   208
12.11 The 'Perimeter' Question   215
12.12 The 'Different Variable Names' Question   215

List of Tables

4.1   Ratio of Loosely-defined to Well-defined Goals for
the Case Study Pupils (Pupil-devised Tasks)   64

4.2   Ratio of Real-World to Abstract Goals for the Case
Study Pupils (Pupil-devised Tasks)   64

5.1   Overview of Case Study Pupils' Solutions to the
'Four Squares' Task at the end of each Year of Study   80

8.1   Analysis of Results of the 'M' Debugging Task for
Longitudinal Case Study Pupils   130

8.2   Analysis of Results of the 'M' Task for Extended
Network Pupils   134

9.1   Categories of Intervention   142

9.2   Percentage of Interventions Categorised by
Motivation, Reflection and Direction   144

10.1   Ratio of Loosely-defined to Well-defined Goals for
the Case Study Pupils   165

10.2   (a) Task Analysis for Sally and Janet's 'Arrow' Task   169
       (b) Task Analysis for George and Asim's 'Arrow' Task   169

12.1   Case Study Pupils' Solutions to Individual Logo
Programming Tasks by Reference to Variable Use   212

12.2   Classification of Case Study and Comparison Groups'
Responses to Structured Interview   214

Acknowledgements

We would like to thank all the pupils who participated in this study. Without them our work could never have taken place. We also wish to acknowledge the enormous contribution to our research of our colleague Joan Evans who worked with us throughout the three years of the Logo Maths Project.

We are indebted to the Leverhulme Trust for providing the funding for our research. We would also like to thank the teachers in the schools in which we carried out our fieldwork; for their inspiration and support and for allowing us to share with them in their mathematics classrooms the richness of the Logo environment. In particular we would like to thank Julie-Anne Edwards and Keith Jones from the Mathematics Department of North Westminster School for supporting us whilst we carried out our longitudinal case study.

We are also indebted to Martin Davies of the Media Resources Department of North Westminster School, without whose help it would have been impossible to collect our data. In addition the technical advice of Lindsey Whittome of the Institute of Education, London University, has been invaluable. We also thank all the colleagues and students with whom we have discussed our ideas and in particular Richard Noss for his enthusiasm for our work and for 'being around' when we needed feedback.

Our special thanks to Lulu Healy for her comments on this book and to Ann McDougal for all her patience and support in producing the final draft.

We are indebted to the following companies for lending us equipment:

Commodore Business Machines
Research Machines Limited
Sinclair Research Machines

1

General Introduction

> Computers are not boring ... that's why a lot of people like
> them ... *and* they wouldn't ask you why you did it ... some
> teachers, they do ... they just keep on and on at you.
>
> Pupil, aged 11 years

Computers are part of our everyday life – at home, in the
work-place and in schools. Stories of the enthusiasm generated by
computer use in our classrooms abound. The interactive
environment and the colourful graphics make computer-based
learning exciting and different. There is a new involvement in
learning of pupils, teachers and parents: there are new challenges,
new ideas, new ways of thinking and a revitalisation of the
educational debate. It is probably true to say that the computer has
been a catalyst for educationalists to question assumptions about
pupil potential to construct their own knowledge and pose their
own problems. The old arguments between discovery and
expository approaches, pupil autonomy and teacher guidance have
taken on a new lease of life.

Since the introduction of computers in schools in the UK there
has been a shift towards the use of general purpose computer
applications software in schools rather than content specific
software. At the same time, there has been a trend towards
computer use across the curriculum rather than within a specialised
topic area such as Information Technology Awareness or Computer
Studies. In tandem with this second trend are calls for the computer
to be part of day-to-day classroom equipment and not tied up
within computer laboratories. These are general trends about
computer use. They are, however, relevant when we consider
computer use for mathematics.

Computers are now considered to be necessary tools in mathematics classrooms and the use of the computer is specifically mentioned in several of the attainment targets of the National Curriculum for Mathematics; for example, use the computer to generate and transform 2-D shapes; use spreadsheets or other computer facilities to explore number patterns (Mathematics in the National Curriculum DES 1989). Although provision inevitably varies across the country, it will not be long before every classroom in both primary and secondary schools has easy access to a bunch of computers which can be used for (amongst other things) developing mathematical learning.

In line with the above trends there is evidence of an upsurge in the use of Logo in both primary and secondary schools in the UK and internationally. Logo is not only used for general educational purposes but also specifically for mathematics. Introducing Logo into mathematics classrooms is seen as a way of providing opportunities for mathematical investigation, encouraging discussion and project work and generally making mathematics a more open and practical subject, accessible and popular to more pupils. Logo is also appropriate as a medium for learning some areas of mathematical content and again examples of Logo are given in the National Curriculum for Mathematics, appearing in all the Key Stages within number, algebra shape and space: for example, Logo is suggested as a vehicle to learn to navigate in 2-D space, to explore simple functions and transformation geometry, to recognise and draw angles, regular polygons and other shapes and to begin to understand co-ordinate geometry. Primary and Secondary teachers are increasingly using Logo (particularly Turtle Graphics) as a natural part of their everyday practice. There is, however, very little published material available concerning the potential of Logo for teaching mathematics and the implications of its use for classroom practice – at least material based on any sort of systematic study. Bringing computers into classrooms inevitably raises a host of questions. What are the learning goals and how do they fit into the curriculum? What are the likely pitfalls and obstacles to learning? What role should the teacher adopt? How should pupils be organised and if they work in pairs what are the implications for the management of learning? It is hoped that this book will go some way towards answering these questions.

This book is about learning mathematics in a Logo environment and learning Logo in a mathematics environment. Within this framework we will raise issues of how pupils learn in pairs with computers in mathematics classrooms. In order to do this we will take into account the interrelated roles of the teacher, the computer feedback and the peer interaction in the pupils' learning. We aim to discuss fundamental questions about the use of the computer in school in terms of cognitive and affective pupil response, the teacher's role and the computer's potential as a catalyst for change in pupil/teacher relations and in pupil involvement in mathematics.

The book is derived from the findings of the Logo Maths Project (1983-6). This was a three-year longitudinal investigation of the use of Logo in the secondary school mathematics classroom. The main focus of the project was to discover whether and under what conditions the computer language Logo could be used as an aid to pupils' understanding of mathematics. Thus Logo was considered not only as a tool for learning mathematics – but also as a tool which had to be studied in its own right. Its use brings with it new ways of thinking, new representations of mathematics, new approaches to learning – and possibly new constraints and conceptual obstacles.

The Logo Maths Project studied pupils from age 11–14 years who used Logo as part of their secondary school mathematics curriculum. Longitudinal case studies were undertaken of eight pupils throughout the three years of the Project. These case study pupils worked in pairs at the computer during their 'normal' mathematics lessons. They had no experience of Logo prior to their involvement in the project and indeed there was no Logo in the mathematics curriculum of the school before 1983. In the 1990s the situation is rather different and many children are learning Logo in the junior school – but doubtless tackling very similar challenges to those faced by our rather older children. All the pupils' Logo work was organised and observed by one of the research team, although throughout the longitudinal study discussions with the class teacher provided an invaluable source of ideas and feedback. The research was extended into a wider network of eight classrooms during the second and third years of the project in order to study the Logo activity in classrooms where the responsibility for the Logo work was with the mathematics teacher rather than with the research team and to observe similarities and differences in patterns of learning.

The Logo Maths Project started with a very general aim – that of increasing understanding of how Logo might provide an environment for the experiential learning of mathematics. Within this framework, we set out to explore:

- the nature and extent of collaborative learning in a small group context when pupils worked with Logo; that is, the motivation and satisfaction deriving from the group involvement in the task and the nature of the interactions between pupils and the language used;
- the problem-solving strategies used by the pupils in the Logo programming environment;
- the nature and consequences of teacher interventions in the learning process;
- the potential of Logo to facilitate understanding of some specific mathematical concepts;
- gender differences in the pupils' approach to programming and problem-solving with Logo.

In this book the findings of the Logo Maths Project will be placed in a wider theoretical perspective focusing on issues such as:

- What mathematics can pupils come to understand in a Logo environment?
- Which problem-solving strategies do pupils use?
- How can pupils learn to work together, to challenge each other's ideas, to argue and elaborate their thoughts?
- Can a Logo programming environment help teachers understand pupils' mathematical conceptions and make appropriate decisions as to subsequent action?

The chapters of the book will follow a general pattern: discussion of a central issue in mathematics education, some appropriate illustration from the research of the Logo Maths Project and finally suggestions for classroom practice.

2

The Logo Maths Project

LOGO AS A PROGRAMMING ACTIVITY

Logo is a programming language derived from the Lisp family. It was developed by Papert and Feurzig in the Artificial Intelligence Laboratory at the Massachussetts Institute of Technology in the late 1960s and was designed so as to provide a mathematical environment accessible to children of all ages and abilities. Until quite recently Logo was only available on large and expensive mainframe computers but it is now widely available for the microcomputer.

The most publicised feature of Logo is its ability to control either a floor or a screen turtle. The turtle is controlled by the turtle graphics subset of the language. The introduction to Logo through turtle graphics provides an important visual dimension to programming. The following is an example taken from one pupil's beginning Logo session. The pupil has used the Logo commands FD, BK ... to draw the picture produced in Fig. 2.1. These commands were introduced into the computer in direct mode and the typing in of each command produced an immediate effect on the screen. This beginning stage of direct interaction with the computer is very important if pupils are to develop an understanding of the sequential processes involved in programming in Logo. If the pupil is satisfied with these commands he or she can define a procedure (Fig. 2.1b). In the versions of Logo used as part of the Logo Maths Project a procedure was defined in 'editor mode'. Modifications and debugging of the procedure were also carried out in this mode.

Fig. 2.1 The Letter F

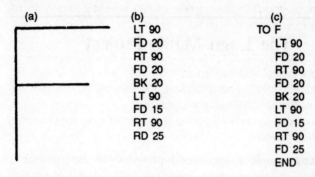

(a)	(b)	(c)
	LT 90	TO F
	FD 20	LT 90
	RT 90	FD 20
	FD 20	RT 90
	BK 20	FD 20
	LT 90	BK 20
	FD 15	LT 90
	RT 90	FD 15
	RD 25	RT 90
		FD 25
		END

Although turtle graphics will be, for most children, the entry point to Logo the geometry of turtle graphics can be pursued to a very high level (Ableson, diSessa, 1981). Appendix 1 presents an overview of the main Logo commands used within this book.

As a programming language the most important features of Logo are:

It is procedural and extensible. A procedure is a group of commands which have been given a name (the procedure name). The procedure commands can consist of Logo primitives or other procedures. Nested layers of procedures can be defined and throughout this book we shall refer to a procedure which is part of another procedure as a subprocedure. We shall also refer to the procedure which contains other procedures as a superprocedure. Procedures can communicate with each other via variable input and output (these are discussed more fully in Chapter 12). It is the procedural nature of Logo which enables the programmer to design structured programs.

It is interactive. Any Logo primitive or procedure is executed by typing it into the computer so the feedback is immediate and errors can be corrected as they occur.

The data structure of Logo is lists. A list consists of an ordered sequence of elements which may be numbers, words or other lists. Lists provide a powerful means to create complex data structures.

It is functional. In a functional language such as Logo the underlying model of an operation is a mathematical function. This is discussed more fully in Chapter 12.

It is recursive. The facility to use recursive procedures enables brief and elegant programs captivating the central structure of a problem to be used in complex structures.

Logo was specifically designed to provide 'a natural environment for an experimental approach to mathematical ideas and processes' (Feurzig *et al.*, 1969) and a context for the use of the general heuristics of analysis, planning and review.

It was decided to choose Logo as the programming language for the following reasons:

* the turtle graphics microworld provides the best available introduction to computer programming for mixed ability classes; it is accessible and highly motivating;
* the procedural and extensible nature of Logo encourages the breaking down of problems into parts and the use of the part solutions as building blocks of alternative structures - all important mathematical activities;
* debugging is aided by the procedural nature of Logo and is encouraged because of the powerful editing and interactive facilities available in Logo.

LOGO AND LEARNING MATHEMATICS

It has been widely maintained that children can learn mathematics ideas through Logo programming. The Logo environment is mathematically rich and because it is also interactive potentially well suited for mathematical exploration. In addition the microworld of turtle graphics within Logo provides for a wide range of mathematical concepts which are dynamic and thus more accessible to pupils.

When the Logo Maths Project started in 1983 previous research in this area could be divided into two broad categories:

* The investigation (mainly at the upper primary level) of the problem-solving strategies and the processes of mathematical thinking that children develop while learning Logo. Such approaches viewed Logo as a conceptual framework for the learning of mathematics (Feurzig *et al.*, 1969; Papert *et al.*, 1979; Papert, 1980).

• The investigation (mainly at early secondary level) into the use of Logo as a modelling tool in order to facilitate the learning of mathematical topics in the school curriculum (Howe *et al.*, 1980; Hartley, 1980).

As well as a difference in focus these two approaches were also distinguished by the degree of structure imposed on the learning environment – the studies devoted to investigating Logo as a modelling tool for the learning of mathematics tended to adopt a much tighter prescribed sequence of learning.

The results of these early research studies are wide ranging and difficult to summarise succinctly. The Brookline Logo Project (Papert *et al.*, 1979) identified a range of mathematical concepts used by the 11- to 12-year-old children in the project (including quantitative and qualitative notions of length and angle), but noted that in several instances a child was not aware of the embedded mathematical concepts used in their programming activity. This early finding has been reinforced by, for example, Leron (1983, 1985), Pea and Kurland (1983), who suggested that some of the powerful ideas of the language do not come naturally to children and that some of the potential of the language for either the understanding of mathematical concepts or as a context for mathematical processes may be missed within a completely unstructured approach. However, within the more structured studies only Hartley (1980) showed significant superiority for his Logo group on all measures of achievement (in directed number and fraction), although Howe *et al.* (1980) reported an overall improvement in the mathematical performance of the girls. An increased willingness and confidence in discussing mathematical problems was also found in an earlier study by the same research group (Howe *et al.*, 1980). With this background of research literature in mind we decided in the Logo Maths Project to seek a balance of pupil-initiated exploration and teacher-initiated structure in the learning of both computational and mathematical ideas.

We believe that the ability to take responsibility for one's actions, to take risks and see what happens, to experiment and find out for oneself are all crucial elements for effective learning, that is, learning that can be used flexibly and creatively at a later date. The overall aim for our interventions within the Logo activities was therefore to leave the control for learning with the learner in order to build up autonomy and reduce teacher-dependence. Pupils were initially allowed the freedom to devise their own goals and simply supplied with handouts on the Logo language as support. As the Project progressed we used more structured tasks to introduce the pupils to new powerful ideas, although still aiming to build an environment in which the pupils had the confidence and space to make sense of these ideas for themselves, largely within collaborative group work.

Thus in summary, we recognised the importance at the outset of some unstructured pupil-centred activity, allowing pupils the opportunity to explore in their own learning style and build up confidence in and control over the language, and some more structured activities with well-defined learning objectives. We also recognised the need for the integration of the computer activity with the 'normal' classroom mathematics activity – as opposed to its separation in time and location.

DESIGN OF THE LOGO MATHS PROJECT

The effects of the computer in the classroom are little understood and certainly at the secondary school level there is still little available research on the subject. As we were carrying out our work in an area in which technology, pedagogy and approach to mathematical content were all innovatory it was decided that case study research was the only appropriate methodology. This methodology, which has been increasingly used in educational research in Britain, allows systematic consideration of a wide range of concerns – all of which must be addressed in any investigation of Logo 'in action' in the classroom.

The Logo Maths Project consisted of two main strands:

- A longitudinal case study of four pairs of pupils (aged 11–14 years) followed throughout their first three years of secondary schooling during which time the researchers planned and monitored all the Logo work.
- An extended two-year (starting in the second year of the Project) study of thirty-two pairs of pupils taken from eight separate classrooms (eight pupils from each classroom) in which the mathematics teachers, after discussion with the research team, were responsible for the pupils' learning of Logo.

In addition during the first year of the Project, we undertook case studies of a further four pairs of pupils (aged 11–12 years) from one other inner London comprehensive school.

The Case Studies

For the case studies, we chose to work in a London comprehensive school with a mixed intake of pupils. The mathematics department in the school was held in high regard. The school followed the SMILE scheme (School Mathematics Independent Learning Experience[1]) so the mathematics classes were organised in mixed ability groups. As a result of consultations in the school a research class was chosen on the basis of the experience and good practice of the mathematics teacher concerned, and her willingness to participate in the study. This teacher had no prior experience of Logo.

The pupils in the research class worked either in groups or individually. It was therefore relatively straightforward to introduce two computers into the classroom. These computers were placed in the corner of the room and became part of the 'normal' mathematical activity within the class.

At the beginning of the first term of the Project the research team worked in the research classroom in order to become familiar with the pupils' normal work routine and to gain acceptance from the pupils and the teacher. After some initial work with larger groups it was decided that pupils should normally work in pairs at the computer. This arrangement promised to enhance the possibility of each pupil participating in the Logo activity. With groups larger than two it seemed very likely that individual pupils would find it difficult to take a turn at the keyboard or be able to make a decision in response to screen output. It was also decided that some activities would be planned so as to naturally involve cooperation between a larger number of pupils and some individual work would be undertaken in the university laboratory for comparative research purposes.

All the class took turns, in pairs, to work at the computer whilst the remainder of the class continued with their SMILE activities. The pairs were chosen by the mathematics teacher on the basis of trying to build effective working partnerships, taking into account factors such as friendship patterns, complementary learning styles and personality factors. For the first few weeks of the Logo work the researchers worked with all of the pairs in the class in turn, giving each pair a simple handout (Fig. 2.2) during their first Logo session and encouraging the pupils to explore these commands freely. We did not give the pupils any goals at this early stage, since we wanted to observe the variety and types of projects that pupils would spontaneously choose for themselves. In November 1983 four pairs of pupils were chosen from all of the pupil pairs in the class to serve as the longitudinal case study pairs. This choice was governed by the need to have a spread of mathematical attainment and an equal number of boys and girls. Two single-sex pairs were chosen and two mixed pairs. The intention was to follow systematically the programming activity of these four pairs of pupils throughout their first three years of secondary schooling and collect data concerning their other mathematical work.

Fig. 2.2 Beginning Logo Handout

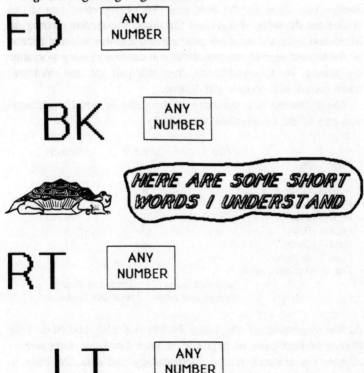

The research team consisted of three members, all of whom took turns to act as a participant observer within the research classroom. We aimed to be present at every programming session of each case study pair. The researchers were responsible for the pupils' learning of Logo – they planned the Logo activities, monitored and discussed the pupil progress, both amongst the team and with the class teacher, and assisted the pupils when necessary. Being present in the classroom over such a period of time also enabled the researchers to see how ideas had spread, how pupils worked in the non-computer context and generally obtain a 'feel' for the classroom climate.

In practice it was not possible to follow the four pairs of pupils as planned because of complications in the school. The boy and the girl in the mixed pair belonging to the lowest attainment band both left the school after the first year of research. They were replaced by a 'similar' pair (Shahidur and Ann) – one of whom, Ann, left at the end of the second year. The boy, Shahidur, was then paired with another boy, Ravi, for the third year. We only present data in this book from the work of Ravi and Shahidur. The second mixed pair, Linda and Jude, did not work productively together towards the end of the second year of the project so it became necessary to change the pairing. We followed Linda, from this pair, into the third year when paired with another girl, Elaine.

The following is a summary of the years in which each pupil was part of the Longitudinal Case Study:

	Year 1	Year 2	Year 3
Pupil 1 (Sally)	√	√	√
Pupil 2 (Asim)	√	√	√
Pupil 3 (George)	√	√	√
Pupil 4 (Janet)	√	√	√
Pupil 5 (Jude)	√	√	—
Pupil 6 (Ravi)	—	—	√
Pupil 7 (Linda)	√	√	√
Pupil 8 (Shahidur)	—	√	√

The working pairs were:

Sally and Janet	Linda and Jude
George and Asim	Ravi and Shahidur

At the beginning of the Logo Project we also undertook case studies of four pairs of pupils in another London comprehensive school. The research setting, methodology and data collection in this school was similar to that described above – except that four computers were used in the classroom, rather than two, and the school although organised on a mixed ability basis was following a different mathematics scheme (School Mathematics Project $11-16^2$). The pairs followed in this school were Panos and John; Beryl and Tracy; Festus and Lloyd, and Ray and Helena. Data was only collected for one year in this school. In the following chapters we shall refer to this second school as school B and the pupils from this school as the 'first year case study pairs'. We shall refer to the main research school as school A and the pupils from this school as the 'longitudinal case study pairs'.

Collection of Data

Once the case study pupils had been chosen video recordings were made of every one of their Logo sessions. This was done by connecting the video recorder between the computer and the monitor. In addition both pupils wore a microphone connected to the video recorder. Thus the videos consisted of all the programming work of the pupils overlaid with the pupils' discussions. These videos formed the core of the research data. Given this data collection it was possible for the researchers to move away from the computer and observe from a distance, when appropriate, secure in the knowledge that the pupils' spoken language and computer commands were being recorded. The video recordings were, however, supported by the following data: hard copies of the pupils' written procedures and graphical output; pupils' written notes; researcher's notes of each Logo session; structured audiotaped interviews of each individual case study pupil carried out at the end of each year of the project; profiles of case study pupils built up from audiotaped interviews with the class teacher.

In order to build up a profile of the longitudinal case study pupils over the three years of the study, we conducted structured interviews with each pupil at the end of each year of the study. We also had valuable and frequent discussions with the mathematics teachers and class tutors together with audiotaped yearly interviews. Finally, data was obtained from the work of the pairs on specific tasks administered individually or in pairs once a year when the case study pupils visited the university.

Analysis of Longitudinal Case Study Data

All the video recordings were transcribed and as this transcript data was being produced we developed procedures of analysis. This transcript data has been invaluable for the following reasons:

- The pupil language, teacher interventions and computer interactions are recorded simultaneously and so can be analysed together in order to identify relationships.

- Analysis is possible of the longitudinal development of the pupils' understandings with respect to specific mathematics or programming concepts by reference to their use of the ideas in a variety of situations. When a pupil misconception is identified by reference to the transcripts its antecedents can be traced back within the preceding transcripts in order to try to interpret the pupil behaviour and suggest contributory factors.

- Comparisons can be made between pupil pairs in terms of programming outcomes and style for the same programming task; for example, the balance of planning and 'hands-on' activity.

We developed from the transcript data the following 'a posteriori' categories in order to provide a framework for the analysis of the interdependent roles of the teacher, the computer and the pupil pair collaboration: categories of intervention (these are described in Chapter 9); categories of programming activity (these are described in Chapter 4); categories of pupil discourse (these are described in Chapter 7). These categories, were initially developed during the first year of the Project and were refined as the research progressed.

The Extended Study

We recognised that our continuous presence as researchers in the case study schools was likely to affect the 'normal classroom' situation. For this reason we extended our research into a wider network of eight first-year mathematics classrooms taken from eight London comprehensive schools, to note the similarities and differences in response to the Logo activities in classrooms where the responsibility for the Logo work was with the mathematics teacher rather than with the researchers. The eight mathematics teachers involved met together with the researchers to plan a common approach to the introduction of Logo. Thus the intended curriculum was similar in terms of tasks, activity and mode of working as in the case study schools. The extended network classes lagged one year behind the intensive case study class, so the results from the case study work informed the overall strategy for intervention and the classroom materials used in the extended network classes. Six of the extended network classes were in mixed London comprehensive schools and one in an all-boys' comprehensive school.

Within each of the extended network classes, four pairs of pupils were designated and whenever a designated pair worked at the computer during a mathematics lesson the class teacher collected data on the planning work carried out by pupils, a record of any procedures written, a completed checklist on type of programming activity, level of collaboration, level of motivation, and extent of intervention.

The extended network data was used to test out hypotheses developed from the case study data. In addition, the extended network pupils were used as a sample to collect data on: pupil attitude to mathematics within a Logo class; differences in pupils' Logo programming styles; differences in classroom climate and teacher response to the introduction of Logo.

This book is derived from the combined results of all the case studies augmented by the extended network data. Most of the examples presented throughout the book are, however, taken from the work of the longitudinal case study pupils as these are the pupils for which the most detailed data are available.

NOTES

1 In the SMILE (School Mathematics Independent Learning Experience) curriculum pupils work at their own individual level. The pupils' work is set from a matrix taken from the 1500 SMILE tasks. These tasks are arranged in topics and levels of difficulty.

2 The SMP (School Mathematics Project 11–16) scheme is also partly an individualised learning curriculum. During the first two years of secondary school pupils worked individually on small topic booklets designed 'to enable pupils to work from them directly at their own pace but also provide scope for group work and teacher-led class activities'.

3

Selected Logo Projects

INTRODUCTION

In this chapter we present a story about each case study pair in order to set the later work described in the book in context. We say a little about each individual child from the basis of our own observations interleaved with comments from their mathematics teacher and extracts from the pupil interviews. We also describe the way each pair of pupils tended to work together, the roles they adopted and what they felt about their partners and their collaboration together. Finally, for each pair we give a description of a Logo project which we have chosen as 'typical' for that pair – in terms of type of goal, quality of peer interaction and reaction to teacher intervention. The projects also provide insight into pupil strategies, how they set 'local' goals within their overall framework, make conjectures and test them out, degoal or debug depending on how they feel about the computer feedback and also in the process of their activity come to understand some specific mathematical and programming concepts. We have highlighted what we see as significant parts of the stories in terms of the pupils' subsequent development.

SALLY AND JANET: 'STARBUSTER'

Sally and Janet were two of our longitudinal case study pupils. Sally was exceptionally shy, probably very able, but her inability to articulate her ideas made it difficult for her mathematics teacher to 'get in touch' with her true potential. Sally was certainly lacking in confidence and often during her Logo programming made comments like 'it won't work'. She enjoyed mathematics but was not someone who showed her feelings. Her mathematics teacher said of her, 'She always works sensibly and quietly but without any apparent enthusiasm or self motivation – perhaps just a reflection of her very quiet personality.' Janet on the other hand was a very chatty and sociable girl. Her attainment in the class was average although her teacher said of her, 'I would like to think that using Logo has helped her in the sense that she is quite a bubbly personality and it has given her a vent for her being able to be herself and have ideas in a mathematical context, which is not how she viewed doing mathematics would be.' Sally and Janet worked together throughout the three years of the Project. Initially there was not much spoken language from Sally during the sessions but we learned that she talked more if we moved away from the computer. Later in the Project she became more assertive in trying to explain her ideas to Janet.

We asked both girls in individual interviews if they would prefer working on their own at the computer than working together. Janet said, 'Well I reckon it wouldn't be as good . . . because we both can do different things and so when you put it together you get a better thing than you would on your own.' Janet also told us that she thought that she learned more from Sally's explanations than she would from a teacher's: 'Like a teacher would tell you and go off . . . if Sally told me she'd stay and she'd help me . . . and we help each other . . . we like teachers but we don't like teachers . . . if you know what I mean.' Sally said of her work with Janet: 'There's always like a little argument between us to see what . . . usually I'm wrong . . . umm we're supposed to turn LEFT and Janet thinks we're supposed to turn RIGHT . . . usually I'm thinking about something different as well . . . so I get it wrong.'

Our analysis of the three years of transcript data has demonstrated the different roles which Sally and Janet took when they were collaborating together. Sally made most of the mathematical decisions; she tended to sit back and reflect or work things out using paper and pencil. After a detailed analysis of the data in relation to turtle turn we discovered that Sally made *every* decision about how much to turn the turtle with the result that Janet was very uncertain about this (see Chapter 8). Janet, however, was often the one who nudged the pair into using a new programming

17

idea, for example variable. She was more experimental and willing to have a go. She also tended to be the typist and in so doing automatically dealt with the precision required for the Logo syntax. As a consequence of this when we gave the girls tasks to work on individually, we discovered that Sally had considerable problems with Logo syntax and often needed help with these details.

The following project is an example of the way in which Sally and Janet worked together, how they negotiated ideas whilst interacting with the computer and built up to goals without an 'a priori' decision about the final product.

At the beginning of their second year of learning Logo, after approximately 20 hours of hands-on time, Sally and Janet decided to define a procedure to draw a star. They succeeded in doing this and defined:

Fig. 3.1 STAR

```
TO STAR
    REPEAT 4 [FD 40 LT 144]
    FD 40
    END
```

It is interesting to note the structure of their final procedure which reflected the process by which it had been constructed. They had built up the non-state-transparent[1] star in direct drive and then used the REPEAT command to tidy up the commands in the editor. They had used this very same strategy previously when working on a project to draw a rotated polygon pattern. They then used this procedure in an exploratory fashion to build a new pattern. They entered STAR, STAR, STAR, STAR, STAR, counting as the pattern emerged until they obtained a complete pattern. Finally the pair defined this as superstar, called SS:

Fig. 3.2 SS, Superstar

```
TO SS
    REPEAT 5 [STAR]
    END
```

Janet talked about the procedure STAR as an 'upside-down star' and Sally as a 'backward star' and between them they decided to draw a 'forward star'. They again worked in direct drive drawing a non-state-transparent star, turning right instead of left when they came to write it in the editor. For some reason, they made this procedure, FS, state-transparent:

Fig. 3.3 FS, Forward Star

```
TO FS
    REPEAT 5[FD 40 RT 144]
END
```

They then defined 'super forward star', SFS, with the same structure as SS:

Fig. 3.4 SFS, Super Forward Star (First Attempt)

```
TO SFS
    REPEAT 5 [FS]
END
```

They discovered that SFS did *not* give them a rotated pattern as expected and tried to debug it. For the SFS procedure to work in the same way as SS – because of the unplanned state transparency of FS – they would need to change FS to make it non-state-transparent. However, they did not see this and simply added an FD 40 to the last line of SFS:

Fig. 3.5 SFS, Super Forward Star (Second Attempt)

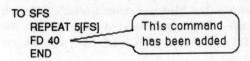

```
TO SFS
    REPEAT 5[FS]
    FD 40          This command
    END            has been added
```

When this still did not give a rotated star the pair reflected on the structure of FS, compared it with STAR and finally modified it to:

Fig. 3.6 FS (Modified)

```
TO FS
   REPEAT 4 [FD 40 RT 144]
   FD 40
   END
```

When they tried this out it drew their desired image but because they had not deleted the final line FD 40 from SFS the turtle ended at B in Fig. 3.4. By chance they had incorporated an interface into SFS!

They now had two modules to 'play with' and once again the pair wanted to make sense of their modules by typing them in and seeing what might happen.

Janet entered SS SFS, saying, 'Now what happens if we did this?' The two stars were drawn one on top of the other.

We intervened at this point to suggest that they define a procedure for this new module. This was the first time that they had defined a superprocedure with two levels of nested subprocedures. They called it superduperstar, SDS:

Fig. 3.7 SDS, Superduperstar

```
TO SDS
   SS
   SFS
   END
```

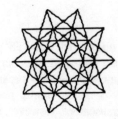

Because of the lucky chance of the FD 40 left on the end of SFS, the interface for another superduperstar was set up!

Janet then used the new module Superduperstar in direct drive. She typed SDS but then 'dropped down a level'. Although she wanted another SDS she entered SS, SFS, the subprocedures of SDS rather than SDS itself. SDS was not yet a word in her vocabulary!

She typed:

```
SDS
SS
SFS
SS
SFS
```

The chance 'bug' (i.e. the unplanned FD 40 at the end of the SFS procedure) generated the new exploratory activity by moving modules through a translation. The bug meant that the interface between modules did not have to be considered or made explicit.

Watching the new pattern emerge on the screen and the structure of the computer input, Janet said, 'Wait a minute... that is Superduperstar SDS... so the next one that's got two can be Superduperduperstar SDDS... the next one can be Superduperduperduperstar SDDDS.'

She saw a generalisation of her pattern and invented a language to describe it – a language which now incorporated Superduperstar. She defined the following procedures immediately without trying them out in direct drive.

Fig. 3.8 SDDS

```
TO SDDS
    REPEAT 2 [SDS]
    END
```

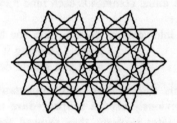

Fig. 3.9 SDDDS

```
TO SDDDS
    REPEAT 3 [SDS]
    END
```

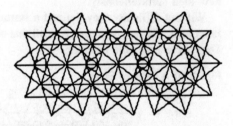

Janet then said, 'What we've made today is star (STAR) and forward star (FS) and SFS and SS... then the other one was SDS and SDDS and SDDDS... right now what we're going to do...?'

At this point we intervened to show them how to define a general procedure:

```
TO SDNS :N
    REPEAT :N [SDS]
    END
```

This formalisation exactly matched the pair's activity and the girls accepted it quite naturally. We encouraged them to 'make sense' of this new procedure by trying it out with different

inputs. They then decided to draw a row of SDS patterns across the screen. They moved the turtle to the left-hand side of the screen keeping a careful record of their commands. This tactic was derived from experience – they knew that if they wanted to start again they would need to repeat the same commands, so systematic recording was now an automatic activity for the pair. Finally the pair entered:

    SDNS 9

They were delighted at the line of stars and tried it out several times in an experimental way. In order to draw this line of Superduperstars the two girls had had to move the turtle to the top left corner of the screen as mentioned above. They had to repeat the initial commands each time they wanted their pattern.

Intervention: 'Now to stop you having to go through all that again ... moving it from there to there ... what you should do is write a procedure ... '

This intervention was important because the pair had not previously used a subprocedure to define 'startup' commands. In later sessions, they showed that they were able to use this new idea spontaneously.

Without difficulty they defined a startup procedure, MOVE, and Janet said, 'So now you can cross all that off ... all that rubbish ... ' They were now able to enter:

Fig. 3.10 A Row of Stars

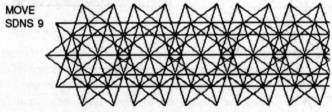

    MOVE
    SDNS 9

They were very excited by the computer response:

    Janet 'Oh this is clever'
    Sally 'It looks like a Christmas cracker'

They decided to draw another row of star patterns and spent a while discussing this. Their collaborative interchange was critical in helping them to define a new interfacing procedure between the two rows for themselves:

Sally 'Now put it back'
Janet 'MOVE we need ... '
Sally 'Not MOVE ... '
Janet 'We'll do MOVE2 ... '
Sally 'We won't do the procedure for it yet ... '
Janet 'We might as well ... '

They tried out the commands for the move in direct drive and Janet again insisted on defining a procedure: 'I'll put it in a procedure ... I might as well ... '

They continued in the same way building up three rows of the pattern defining MOVE3 for the interface between the second and third row after first working out the correct commands in direct mode. Finally they decided to name their pattern of three rows:

Janet 'You give a name to this then.'
Sally 'STARBUSTER.'

Fig. 3.11 STARBUSTER

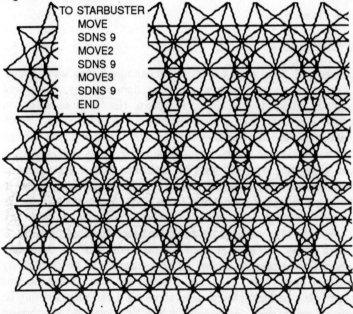

```
TO STARBUSTER
   MOVE
   SDNS 9
   MOVE2
   SDNS 9
   MOVE3
   SDNS 9
   END
```

Figure 3.11 gives their final procedure. In this open-ended project the girls had used three levels of nested subprocedures, had defined a startup procedure and procedures for the interfacing between each row of stars. These ideas were *all* taken up in the later sessions.

23

Overview of Story

This project was one of the favourites of the two girls – they enjoyed the surprises, the challenges and the final result. During the session Sally and Janet used the ideas of modularity and variable; they also defined a startup and an interface procedure. The project evolved during the session partly at least as a result of a chance bug. We believe that the importance of working towards these loosely-defined goals should not be undervalued since programming ideas emerge naturally – even if implicitly. The experience is valuable in itself but also can be built upon at a later stage. When the girls were breaking down a well-defined project into modules, we found that they were able to use these ideas as part of their structured design of the task. Some pupils do not naturally choose to experiment in this way and need encouragement to do so. In contrast, as we discuss in Chapter 5, we found that Sally and Janet needed encouragement to work on more well-defined projects.

GEORGE AND ASIM: 'THE SPIRAL'

George and Asim were two of our longitudinal case study pupils. George was a very confident, articulate, dominant boy who related better to adults than he did to his peers. His favourite subject at school was Craft, Design and Technology (CDT), ''Cos I enjoy making things.' His mathematics teacher considered that George was above average in the class and said, 'He works enthusiastically and perseveres over all sorts of problems with a high level of concentration.' She also said that, 'He is an independent worker to the extent of being a loner and I still think that he doesn't discuss his work enough with others ... even those sharing the same task ... he is highly motivated but he doesn't take on board the ideas of others easily.' George enjoyed mathematics more at secondary school than at primary school but his perception of his own ability was not high, 'I'm OK ... but I'm not the best.' When he was asked what he had enjoyed most about his Logo programming he said, 'Getting away from maths while I'm doing it.' He showed some anxiety about his enthusiasm for computer programming since it diverted him from mathematics – he saw the two activities as separate. When we asked him what he thought about not having a computer in the mathematics class he said, 'Ummmm, I wouldn't like it . . . I suppose people would get on with their maths and do more maths . . . when you're using the computer everyone's walking around.'

Asim was a reserved, studious boy who worried about his mathematics work and wanted to get on and get ahead. English was not his first language. His mathematics teacher considered that he was above average in the class: 'I think Asim's attitude has broadened in the year and he now enjoys the more creative aspects of maths, though he has difficulty in approaching investigative work.' She also said, 'He is a very organised and independent learner . . . highly motivated . . . preferring to think things out for himself.' Asim had a computer at home but only used it for playing games. Mathematics was one of Asim's favourite subjects. Science was his least favourite because he never 'got anything done'. When asked what he liked doing most of all when he was not in school he said, 'Usually I read or revise.' The mathematics teacher said, 'I think Logo has helped him develop the less traditional aspects of learning . . . allowing him scope for independence in setting his own problems and in relating his original narrower view of maths to a broader field.'

At the beginning of the Logo Maths Project, Asim and George did not appear to be collaborating very well when they were working together. This was because George dominated during the 'hands-on' stage. However, as the first week progressed, Asim took a more central role in the planning of projects. When we asked Asim whether he could think of any advantages of working in a pair he said, 'If I'm stuck on something . . . yeah . . . but if I were working on my own I wouldn't have George nagging at me all the time.' At the end of the first year George told us that he would prefer to work on his own: 'I'd like that better . . . because you can do what you want.' We asked him if he was aware that he dominated Asim and he said, 'Yeah . . . it runs in my family.' By the end of the Logo Maths Project the change in the collaboration between Asim and George was quite remarkable. The transcript data shows that Asim was more persistent and did not just give up if George ignored him. George on the other hand learned to listen to Asim's point of view. We know that George and Asim still choose to work together at the computer now that they are in the fourth year of secondary school although they are no longer asked to do so for the purposes of the research.

The following is a description of a session in which George and Asim had chosen to draw a spiral image (Fig. 3.12) from a set of

25

abstract images which we had given them. Although apparently a well-defined closed project, it turned out to be just a starting point for more creative work.

Fig. 3.12 The 'Circular Spiral' Task

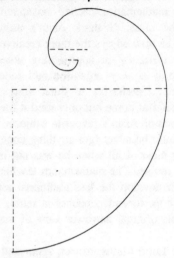

Negotiating a Plan

Before typing in any commands George and Asim negotiated a plan. They both had their own ideas about what to do but needed to come to some common understanding. George suggested that they use the ARCR command to draw the quarter circles, but Asim questioned this decision saying, 'What about using the REPEAT command, it's quicker.' They eventually decided on the ARCR command because they believed that the ARCR command drew an accurate circle and the REPEAT command drew only an approximate circle! Asim then worked out the radii of the quarter circles and told George to type in the following commands:

Fig. 3.13 A First Attempt

```
ARCR 5 90
ARCR 10 90
ARCR 20 90
ARCR 40 90
ARCR 80 90
```

The pair discovered that they should have moved the turtle before starting the spiral in order to fit it all on the screen. They did this, recording the startup commands and entered the sequence again.

Experimenting at the 'Hands-on' Stage

Asim was quite convinced that inputs of 5, 10, 20, 40 and 80 formed a 'correct' *mathematical* sequence to achieve a spiral. He had considered the global structure of the problem and how the different parts should follow a pattern. George, in contrast, argued that there should be a 'nice' representation and that the image on the screen should look *exactly* like the picture. He therefore insisted that they experiment with different sequences so that the output image on the screen matched more closely what was in the booklet. **The two boys evidently had rather different goals in mind.** They tried out the effect of two more sequences of commands as follows:

Fig. 3.14 A Second Attempt

```
ARCR 10 90
ARCR 20 90
ARCR 40 90
ARCR 70 90
ARCR 80 90
```

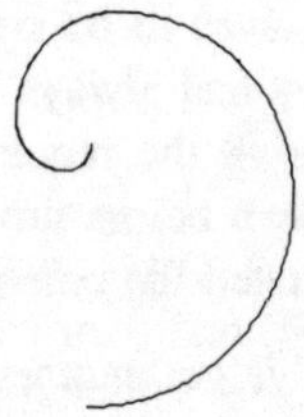

Fig. 3.15 A Third Attempt

```
ARCR 10 90
ARCR 15 90
ARCR 25 90
ARCR 40 90
ARCR 60 90
```

Each time they tried out a new sequence they used the same startup commands. They eventually decided that they should write a separate procedure (START) to do this – this was the first time that this had happened. The pair perceived the startup as a separate module which they would need to keep on using during their experimentation. They had no problem in defining it as a separate subprocedure.

After exploring the effect of different sequences of commands George was still not satisfied: 'How about making ... you know that 80 ... make it 60 ... it'd probably work as well ... ' Asim remained convinced that his sequence was mathematically correct: '80 ... 60 ... it'd be different ... ' George did not like to give in: 'I know, just let's try it ... '

George's persistent disagreement provoked Asim to elaborate his reasons more clearly: 'I know it would be different ... look at that compared to that ... wouldn't it ... everything's twice as big as that ... that's twice as big as that ... that's twice as big as that ... ' At this point George conceded and they reverted to the sequence in Fig. 3.13.

Extending the Goal

The pair had completed the original task but because it had not been preplanned to be an exact representation of a picture they went on to extend the project. This was the first time that they had allowed themselves to be creative whilst working at the computer. In the past they had always been constrained by tightly preplanned projects where all the required computer commands were decided and written down before any hands-on activity.

George initiated the extension:

George   'I've got another idea ... do another one coming round there ... it would be good wouldn't it ... should we do it ... ?' (the spiral from B to C in Fig. 3.16)

Asim   'Mmmmmmm.'

Fig. 3.16 Extending the Spiral

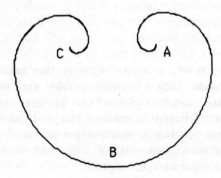

George knew how he was going to achieve this: 'So we just got to reverse all these . . . ' Asim was quite happy with George's work: 'It's looking exciting isn't it?'

A Further Extension

The image on the screen provoked a further extension. Pointing at C and then A (Fig. 3.16) Asim said, 'Hold it . . . why not draw a line from there to there?' Asim meant a straight line but George did not quite understand so he asked: 'From there to there like that . . . ?'

Both boys wanted to close the figure but had different ideas as to how to do this – Asim had in mind a straight line and George a semicircle. After some negotiation Asim raised a quite reasonable objection to George's suggestion that they draw a semicircle between C and A: 'Yeah, but we don't know how big it's going to be . . . ' George's hesitating reply indicated that he was thinking through the problem whilst talking aloud . . . 'Yeah, you're right . . . that's why I don't want to . . . oh wait a sec . . . ' Asim then returned to his suggestion: 'We could draw a straight line . . . '

This comment of Asim's helped George solve the problem of how to draw a circular arc, that is 'carry through his own idea' – 'If we drew a straight line we could find out . . . couldn't we . . . how long that it . . . couldn't we . . . ?' Asim provoked George into articulating his plan more clearly: 'Are we going to do the circle or the straight line . . . ?' George explained, 'We're going to do the straight line to find out how far it is . . . and then rub it back . . . and then we find out how far it is and then we can do it . . . using the ARCR command . . . '

Thus George planned to use a straight line drawn in direct mode to 'calculate' the distance between A and C which could then be used to draw his semicircle. The pair then carried out this strategy. They moved the turtle to C and 'homed in' to A by trial and error. They found in this way that the distance CA was 70 turtle steps.

The boys would have found it difficult to calculate the distance CA using their mathematical knowledge. **They were not 'stuck', however, because in the Logo environment they were able to apply a 'concrete' trial and error approach to achieve their ends. We suggest that this is an important source of motivation when working with Logo – the pupils themselves can find different ways to get over the obstacles they come up against.**

In so doing they do not necessarily learn those things that one might expect – but they still learn and they learn ideas which are functional for their own projects.

In this situation George and Asim found out something new about the nature of ARCR. Having 'measured' CA as 70 they typed ARC 70 180. Until this point the meaning of the first input to ARCR was obviously not clear to them. On seeing the screen output, however, they realised that the first input to the ARCR command was the radius and *NOT* the diameter!

Intervention with a Powerful Idea

When George and Asim had finished drawing in direct drive they wanted to write a procedure. We talked to them about the relationship between the inputs of the ARCR commands in the right-hand spiral and then explained how to write a procedure using a variable input. This had been our hidden agenda for the session although we had not worked out how it could be operationalised! As it happened, the structure of their direct drive commands led naturally to the following procedure:

Fig. 3.17 General Right Hand Spiral (First Attempt)

```
TO ANGLE :NUM
  ARCR :NUM 90
  ANGLE MUL :NUM 2
END
```

Because the boys had 'played around' with different sequences of numbers they had no problem recognising the mathematical structure of their spiral and understanding its formalisation in the program.

We intentionally did not include a conditional STOP statement in the procedure, ANGLE. They tried ANGLE 5 and the spiral carried on drawing, eventually hitting the edge of the screen. This provoked George and Asim to reflect further on the process without any intervention from us.

George   'Oh it's multiplied by two ... oh, we've got ... '
Asim   'What did you do ... what happened ... ?'
George   'It's multiplied by two again ... it didn't stop ... '
Asim   'You want how many times you've got to do it ... ?'

They had a general idea now and needed to focus on particular values:

Intervention 'On which ARCR command does it get too big?'
George '80 ... when it doubles 80 ... '

As this was their first use of the conditional statement we showed them the syntax and they discovered where to insert it into their procedure:

Fig. 3.18 General Right Hand Spiral (Second Attempt)

```
TO ANGLE :NUM
    IF GRQ :NUM 80 [STOP]
    ARCR :NUM 90
    ANGLE MUL :NUM 2
    END
```

They were not at all confident that this procedure would work. George appeared to think that the computer had some magical powers which he could control!

George 'Keep your fingers crossed.'
Asim 'I'm not superstitious.'
George 'Well keep you feet crossed then.'
Asim 'I'm still not superstitious.'
George 'I'm superstitious.'

Nevertheless when this worked without further intervention from us, the pair started on the task of writing a procedure to draw the left-hand spiral. They were aware that they could use the same input. George even realised that they could not use the same conditional statement: 'Miss, we're going to have ... we can't have ... IF GREATER THAN 5 ... 'cos it goes down to 5 ... so what should we have ... below 5 ... ?'

We showed them the 'less than', LSQ, statement in the handbook and they wrote the subprocedure ANGLE2 where the inputs to ARCR were successively divided by 2. Finally they added their last half circle and put all the subprocedures together in a superprocedure SPIRAL (Fig. 3.19).

Fig. 3.19 A Spiral Pattern

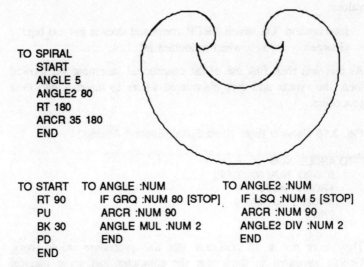

```
TO SPIRAL
    START
    ANGLE 5
    ANGLE2 80
    RT 180
    ARCR 35 180
END
```

```
TO START          TO ANGLE :NUM              TO ANGLE2 :NUM
    RT 90             IF GRQ :NUM 80 [STOP]       IF LSQ :NUM 5 [STOP]
    PU                ARCR :NUM 90                ARCR :NUM 90
    BK 30             ANGLE MUL :NUM 2            ANGLE2 DIV :NUM 2
    PD                END                         END
END
```

Building up a New Goal

George and Asim then proceeded to make sense of their newly
created object on the screen (SPIRAL) – something again they had
never done with their picture goals. They wanted to translate
SPIRAL across the screen and finally wrote a superprocedure
SPIRAL3 (Fig. 3.20). **This was the first time that they had built
up a pattern by moving an already written procedure around
the screen.**

Fig. 3.20 Building up Spiral Patterns

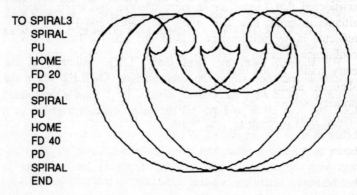

```
TO SPIRAL3
    SPIRAL
    PU
    HOME
    FD 20
    PD
    SPIRAL
    PU
    HOME
    FD 40
    PD
    SPIRAL
END
```

Overview of Story

Much can be learned from this one session with Asim and George. Although we suggested a goal so the pair were initially restricted in their activity they eventually worked more creatively at the computer than they had ever done before. Ironically they usually imposed more restrictions *on themselves* with their own well-defined preplanned picture projects than we would have dreamt of doing! During the session the pair felt free to explore the effect of different processes and different problem solutions and the project required them to use many mathematical and programming ideas such as variable, interface, tail recursion and conditionals. The formalisation arose naturally – as a way of describing their direct mode activity in a clear, concise way – so the boys were able to see the connection between actions and formalisations and to move from one to another in a flexible fashion. We believe that it is important to introduce ideas like recursion within the context of the pupils' own problem-solving activity. Here it happened to emerge naturally. We now recognise, however, that some pupils will need to be directed to work on types of goals in which these ideas are likely to occur.

LINDA AND JUDE/ELAINE: 'THE CUBE'

Linda and Jude were two longitudinal case study pupils. They worked together for the first two years of the project. Linda was a very friendly, talkative girl who was confident with adults. By the end of the first year of the project the mathematics teacher considered that Linda 'has a more positive and more confident attitude to maths now than when she started and I think this is reflected in her performance. I think she suffered from a lack of confidence in maths in primary school which accounts for her low entry grade.' At the beginning of the project she was not confident about her ability to do mathematics: 'I wasn't good at maths at my primary school', but her perception of her ability seemed to change during the year, 'I dunno. I quite like maths ... I'm getting better at it so I'm beginning to enjoy it more ... now I'm getting better at it I find it easier and more fun to do.' Linda's Logo work was very important to her and she displayed her printouts in her bedroom under the heading LINDA'S COMPUTING WORK. She told us that when she talks to her friends in other classes about the computer, 'They sort of get jealous because they don't do it and they really want to do it.' She had tried going to computer club after school, 'But that was Basic and that was sort of difficult . . . it was much harder . . . maybe because Logo was explained to us more than Basic was . . . ' Although during the first year of the project we felt that Linda was gaining confidence in her ability to do mathematics this was not consistently maintained – perhaps at least partly due to the fact that the class did have three changes of mathematics teacher during the three years of the project. From her Logo work we knew that she was very resistant to any form of number manipulation and by the end of the project she told us, 'I'm not too keen on maths 'cos I don't think I am any good at it.' She acknowledged her success with her Logo work and positively enjoyed 'working out sums' in Logo, but was not able to view her activities at the computer as related in any way to her potential in school mathematics.

Jude gave the impression of being a quiet boy although he told us that he had been in quite a lot of trouble at school for 'mucking about'. His mathematics teacher said that 'He is a bubbly personality, tending to mischievous naughtiness with very little ability to concentrate over a period of time.' He was considered by his mathematics teacher to be 'Below average in ability but he has made a consistent steady improvement over the year. His level of motivation depends on the task he is doing, as he sometimes needs constant reminding to concentrate . . . yet often gets engrossed in something . . . there appears to be no pattern to the topic or type of work involved.' Jude was rather neutral about mathematics, 'I like it alright, Miss . . . ', but was more enthusiastic about the Logo activities within his mathematics lessons, ''Cos it was more exciting . . . Miss, 'cos you're just doing the same thing every day when you are writing cards.' He gave another insight into why the computer was important to him: 'It is better than paper to write 'cos it can't get lost as easily as paper.' His mathematics teacher said, 'I think that Logo has improved his ability to concentrate in mathematics.' Jude had used a Sinclair Spectrum at his primary school: 'Sir just gave us maths games and you had to guess the numbers . . . urr, the Logo is much better 'cos that was a bit boring . . . it was just numbers and there was only one computer . . . so if we kids were to go on here at once there was loads of arguing.' He also had a computer at home on which he mostly played games.

To begin with Jude and Linda appeared to value their work together although they never associated with each other when they were not working on the computer. Linda said, 'I think it is easier if you work in pairs . . . 'cos you come up with better ideas', but she did think that she would sometimes like to work with another pairing, 'You could do with a change.' They shared the responsibility for systematically recording their procedure commands and they both recognised that Jude did not find recording easy. Of working on his own Jude said, 'It would be harder . . . 'cos writing down . . . 'cos I found it harder.' Of working with Linda he said, 'Miss, she just tells me what to do and I type it.'

By the end of the second year of the project Linda and Jude were no longer collaborating well together. This was reflected in the increased amount of 'off-task' talk which they engaged in whilst working at the computer. We therefore decided to pair Linda with Elaine, a friend with whom she worked during 'normal' mathematics lessons. Elaine, like Linda, did not find mathematics easy and was very lacking in confidence about her ability. She did not appear to enjoy her normal mathematics, 'Maths is alright, I like it more than I used to . . . 'cos I never really liked it, it's never been one of my favourite subjects.' When we asked her why she now liked maths more she said, ''Cos I've discovered that I hate languages more than maths.' She preferred to work with a partner on the computer, 'If you get stuck you can work it out together.'

In their second session together Linda and Jude decided to draw a cube. **Although this task was very difficult for them they continually returned to this project over a period of three months. We include this example from Linda and Jude's work because it illustrates the high level of persistence towards achieving a goal which was characteristic of their early Logo work. We believe that it was the high level of motivation generated by the cube project which helped Linda and Jude to devise a strategy for debugging procedures.** The following is a summary of the four sessions spread over a period of 10 weeks in which they continually refined their cube until for them it became 'absolutely right'.

In their first session, Linda and Jude tried to draw a cube. Eventually they drew a cube in direct drive producing the following shape:

Fig. 3.21 First Attempt at a Cube

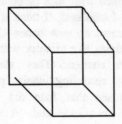

In their next session the pair decided to draw a cube again. In fact they ended up drawing a cuboid in direct drive and keeping a record of their commands. They wrote a procedure from their written record without tidying up distance commands (e.g. they wrote down FD 30 FD 20 instead of FD 50). They introduced a transcribing error into their procedure and when they ran the procedure it produced Fig. 3.22. Linda said: 'What's it doing there ... we never told it to do that.'

Fig. 3.22 First Attempt at a Cuboid

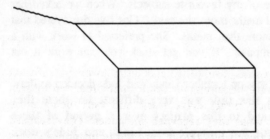

At this stage they did not feel that the bugs in the procedure were their responsibility. They did not look back over their procedure in order to debug it but modified the image on the screen in direct drive.

Two months after their initial attempts at drawing a cube, Linda and Jude decided to draw a cuboid again and started the same process of direct driving and recording on paper. When they wrote the procedure for their cuboid they missed out two commands. On running their buggy procedure this time though they reacted very differently. They tried to debug their procedure by systematically checking the procedure commands with their

written record. However, by trying to correct their bugs they introduced more bugs into their procedure and became very confused. At this stage we intervened to support them in debugging as we realised that without this intervention they were likely to give up and start again from the beginning. They finally produced a working procedure (Fig. 3.23). They were not concerned with the exact appearance of the cuboid although they realised that 'it had not come out properly.'

Fig. 3.23 Second Attempt at a Cuboid

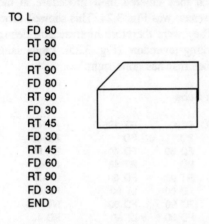

```
TO L
  FD 80
  RT 90
  FD 30
  RT 90
  FD 80
  RT 90
  FD 30
  RT 45
  FD 30
  RT 45
  FD 60
  RT 90
  FD 30
END
```

Four weeks later was the pair's final attempt at drawing a cube. **At this stage they were beginning to think about the step-by-step process within their direct drive work and were being more systematic about what they recorded on paper. They realised that it was worth their while taking care not to introduce errors by lack of attention in the transcribing process. In addition they tidied up commands *before* recording to make things easier.**

At one point Linda did not want Jude to record her trial and error process and she said to him: 'Ummm, don't write this down ... I don't know if it's right.' At a later stage in the session, after typing RT 135 LT 45 LT 45, they discussed what to record:

Jude   'Another 45 again.'
Linda   'Put down ummm ...'
Jude   'Just put LT 45 ... I mean RT 45 ... LT 45 ... I don't know ... LT 45 ... right, now I do the typing ...'

Fig. 3.24 The Cube Revisited

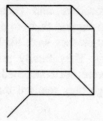

However, they incorrectly recorded LT 45. This was the only bug in their procedure and when they entered their procedure in the computer the image on the screen was Fig. 3.24. This showed them they were *nearly* correct. They were therefore motivated to debug and finally produced a working procedure (Fig. 3.25). Linda said, 'It's the first one of our cubes that has gone right.'

Fig. 3.25 Final Attempt at a Cube

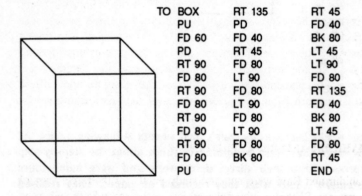

TO BOX	RT 135	RT 45
PU	PD	FD 40
FD 60	FD 40	BK 80
PD	RT 45	LT 45
RT 90	FD 80	LT 90
FD 80	LT 90	FD 80
RT 90	FD 80	RT 135
FD 80	LT 90	FD 40
RT 90	FD 80	BK 80
FD 80	LT 90	LT 45
RT 90	FD 80	FD 80
FD 80	BK 80	RT 45
PU		END

Overview of Session

Linda and Jude set themselves a very difficult task and they enjoyed the challenge of achieving it. When Linda was asked why she said: "Cos we had many tries at it and it kept going wrong ... about ... four times I think to get it absolutely right ... ' When asked why she kept on going, she replied: "Cos we *wanted* to get it right ... 'cos we'd done a 3-D rectangle and we wanted to do a 3-D cube.'

We also asked Jude what was the best thing he had done on the computer and he replied, '*The cube*'. When asked why, he said: 'I don't know, Miss ... 'cos we tried loads of times, Miss ... but it never come out properly ... but the last time we did it, it did come out properly ... '

Overview of Story

This project highlights the importance in terms of motivation and in terms of developing an understanding of process for pupils to work on their own goals during the beginning stages of learning. We also believe that when pupils are at the beginning stages of defining a procedure the teacher has an important role in showing the pupils the potential of debugging. Our observations indicate that without this intervention pupils simply tend to scrap procedures and start again. Linda and Jude gradually took more responsibility for their incorrect work – to begin with it was the computer's fault but later they learned for themselves that if they wanted to minimise the bugs in their procedure then systematic recording was very important. The role of collaboration during the Cube project was important in keeping the project going until the goal was finally achieved. Their final procedure Box is also interesting in other ways – all the turns are multiples of 45 and the lengths were achieved by perceptual strategies rather than analytic ones. These two issues turned out to be very typical of the pair's future work.

SHAHIDUR AND RAVI: 'THE PLANE'

Shahidur and Ravi were not case study pupils for the three years of the project. Shahidur joined the project in the second year when he was paired with Amanda. Then at the end of the second year Amanda left the school and Shahidur started to work with Ravi.

When Shahidur started secondary school he was a very quiet boy who hardly spoke any English. He often missed mathematics lessons so that he could attend an 'English as a second language' lesson. He was rather small for his age and certainly at the beginning of secondary school was not a pupil who would be easily noticed by a teacher. By the third year of the project his English and his confidence had improved remarkably. He became more disruptive in class as if he needed to test the bounds of the system. He was always very enthusiastic about using the computer and when asked what he liked most about his mathematics lessons he said 'computing'. His reply to what do you like least was 'homework'! He became very keen to explore the computer system and at one point was banned from using the computer for several weeks because he had succeeded in erasing some programs from the class disk. At the beginning and throughout the three years of the project his mathematical attainment within the class was very low. In response to the question 'What do you think your mathematics teacher thinks about your maths?' he gave us the impression that he thought that the teacher gave him work which was too easy, 'Even though I could do ... but I was still doing mistakes ... ' When asked what he would like to do when he leaves school he said, 'Well, I want to do like ... a simple job ... maybe as a bank clerk ... ' He loved drawing realistic images in turtle graphics, "Cos I'm quite good at drawing ... I draw the picture and I can do it ... a picture in Logo is easy.' He also very much preferred to choose his projects himself, 'So I can do what I want and what I like.'

At the beginning of the Logo Maths Project we noticed that Ravi appeared to be very disruptive and did not find it easy to settle in class. His mathematical attainment was very low and although this improved his attainment was still below average with respect to the rest of the class. Although he was not initially a case study pupil we did notice that during the beginning stages of learning Logo he often became very frustrated by his work at the computer. He set himself very high standards and became angry by what he perceived as his failure to reach these standards. There was, however, a remarkable change in his computer work as he began to accept the debugging powers of Logo. His concentration level when working in Logo far exceeded that exhibited by him during his 'normal' mathematics work. Ravi preferred to choose his own projects in Logo and he also preferred to work with a partner. His favourite subject at school was graphical communication and when we asked him what that was, he said, 'It's all to do with architecture really ... that's what I want to be ... ' He told us that maths was also a favourite subject although he talked about being 'Only on level 4.' He said that his teacher 'Thought that I was a bit talking too much ... but I got on with my work when I wanted ... and did a lot of homework.'

Shahidur and Ravi appeared to work well together although they did not have the commitment to their collaboration in the same way as George and Asim, for example. **This was probably because they only worked together for six sessions and it is our**

experience that pupils take considerably longer to develop a collaborative relationship. We have chosen 'The Plane' to illustrate Shahidur and Ravi's work because it is both typical of the type of project which they liked to choose for themselves and it also illustrates their considerable persistence in achieving their goal. Both Shahidur and Ravi had a clear idea of what the final image taken from the real world would look like when they started the project and they used Logo as a drawing tool to construct this image.

Shahidur and Ravi together came up with the idea of drawing a plane at the beginning of the session. Shahidur initiated the idea of finding a book from the library with a picture of an aeroplane which they could then copy. Shahidur asked, 'Have you got a book ... shall I quickly nip to the library and get a book of a plane?'

They discussed the images in the book. Having chosen a picture of an aeroplane their plan was to copy it exactly, reproducing it in as much detail as possible. They looked forward to the challenge of their project. Ravi said, 'That one's wicked, boy ... ' The pair then entered a 'hands-on' stage. They were planning at a local level and almost all the computer commands were negotiated before being entered into the computer. Ravi said, 'Shall we start on the back wheel?' and Shahidur replied, 'Yeah ... it's going to be wicked ...'

They started at A (Fig. 3.26) and entered LT 45. Ravi suggested a global strategy. 'We're just doing the main shape ... we're going to put the details on after.' Shahidur agreed: 'Oh, that's a good idea.'

Fig. 3.26 An Aeroplane (this figure shows the final image produced)

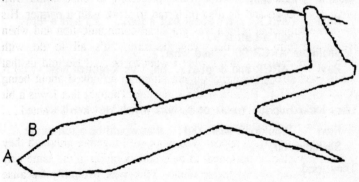

Teacher Intervention

They wanted the plane to be at an angle to the horizontal (see Fig. 3.26). We intervened to suggest that they positioned the plane *after* they had drawn the shape: 'You don't have to draw it at that angle ... 'cos you can make the shape at any angle.' Shahidur did not take up this idea. He obviously did not at this point appreciate the intrinsic nature of turtle geometry – which was not surprising given his limited experience! He said, 'I'm going to draw it at an angle.'

We then suggested that he separate out on his written record the startup and the aeroplane commands. This was an intervention to push towards the idea of subprocedure. 'Remember which commands get it at the right angle and which draw the actual shape.'

They continuously focused on the local detail of the task and in so doing their talk involved language related to estimation of angle and distance. This is illustrated in the following excerpts.

The pair have drawn AB (Fig. 3.26) and Ravi said: 'Now curve ... turn it a degree.' They negotiated the turn:

Shahidur '30?'
Ravi   '45.'
Shahidur 'No, not 45.'

They typed:

LT 35

Shahidur next suggested that they use the ARCR command to obtain the required curvature. They needed to remember the syntax and then to negotiate what to use as inputs for ARCR. Their discussion also indicated that Ravi had a misconception about the angle of a total turn.

Ravi   'ARCR ... it's about half a turn ... it's half a turn ... half a turn is 90.'
Shahidur 'ARCR 90 ... and what?'
Ravi   'ARCR and degrees ... oh, I've forgotten how to do it ... where's the sheet?'

They looked up the syntax on a sheet which was available.

Ravi   'You don't want 180 ... that would be a full circle ...'
Shahidur '60?'

They tried

ARCR 10 60

This was an important step in their solution of the problem. The feedback on the computer screen told them that their angle input was not correct and they immediately responded to this.

Shahidur 'So we need ARCR 10 180.'

They wanted to undo their ARCR command. At this point they did not realise that they could 'add on' another ARCR command, ARCR 10 120, to their original ARCR 10 60 to achieve a total effect of ARCR 10 180.

Shahidur 'How do we get it back?'
Ravi 'The same way as we did before.'
Shahidur 'You have to face it that way first.'
Ravi 'No, just do BK ... ARCR 5 60 ... backwards.'
Shahidur 'It won't work.'
Ravi 'It does ... it's just the same innit? ... The same as when you put the pencil up.'
Shahidur 'No it won't.'

They tried:

RT 180
ARCL 5 60

This did not work so they decided to start again from the beginning. They cleared the screen and typed in the commands from their written record.

When they reached the ARCR they again negotiated their input, pointing at the screen to support their suggestions.

Ravi 'Try 10 90 ... it has to be 90.'
Shahidur '90 is half of 180 is there.'
Ravi 'No, half of 180 is there.'
Shahidur 'No, but 90 will be here.'
Ravi 'Look, that's 180 right ... half of that is there ... '
Shahidur 'Yeah, but what I mean is ... '

Ravi was provoked to justify his suggestions. Interestingly enough he now 'knew' that a full circle was 360!

Ravi 'Look, full circle is there ... 180 is there ... half of 180 is there ... innit ... ?'
Shahidur 'Alright then ... hope it works ... '

ARCR 10 90

They were not satisfied with the effect on the screen and so they started again from the beginning and this time went back to using

ARCR 10 60. Ravi commented: 'It's a bit wonky . . . man . . . '

But this time they continued. By the end of their first session they had drawn Fig. 3.27, having started from the beginning many times. They were always careful not to record on paper until they were certain that the effect of a set of commands was correct and always combined the operations before recording (for example: LT 65 RT 5 RT 5 RT 5 was recorded as LT 50). This showed a development – at their beginning stages of Logo work they recorded all the commands on paper.

Fig. 3.27 An Aeroplane, Part 1

Teacher Intervention

At the end of the session we intervened to suggest that they write a procedure:

> Intervention 'Are you going to be writing a program
> eventually?'
> Ravi   'Yeah.'

They started the next session, however, by entering directly the commands from their written record. **We intervened again with the same suggestion:**

> Intervention 'You might not have another go for a while so I
> want you to try and get it finished and write a
> program . . . '

They still carried on in direct mode! They continued to work with attention to detail, rubbing out when they were not satisfied with the effect of a command or starting again from the beginning.

Ravi 'And then rub it out . . . 'cos it's got to be sort of straightish . . . that's completely round.'

It seemed that we became impatient with their persistence.

Intervention 'It doesn't matter if it's not exactly the same . . . you can put a bit of your own individuality into it.'
Ravi   'No, it's meant to be straight and we done it all round, so it don't look good.'

Shahidur was the pupil who was mainly responsible for ensuring that the written record was systematically kept.

Shahidur 'Now have you wrote everything down? . . . there was RT 90 FD 5 . . . RT 90.'

By the end of the second session they had drawn Fig. 3.28 but **they had *not* written a procedure.** They started their third session by typing in all the commands again. Ravi was concerned about the wing of the aeroplane.

Ravi   'That's too round.'
Shahidur 'It don't matter, just leave it.'
Ravi   'No, we need to change it . . . we don't want it like that . . .'

Fig. 3.28 An Aeroplane, Part 2

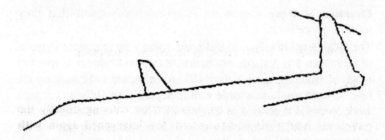

We *again* intervened to suggest that they write a procedure and the intervention was becoming still more directed.

Intervention 'You've got about quarter of an hour before the end of the lesson. If you spend a lot of time trying to get it perfect you won't get it finished . . . so I suggest instead of trying to be a perfectionist . . .

I mean it looks good as it is . . . just try and get it
finished.'

Shahidur began to get tired of Ravi's insistence on an exact match
with the image in the book or possibly Shahidur was more willing
to please the teacher and finish the project by the end of the lesson.
'Leave it . . . I'm getting bored with this . . . do that part . . . ' – but
they still carried on!

By this time the pair had worked out how to 'rub out' a
command produced by ARCR by typing:

```
ARCR 5 90
LT 180
PE
ARCL 5 90
```

Ravi all the time estimated the angle input to the ARCL and ARCR
commands by referring to half and quarter circles. 'It's not even a
half circle.' He was by now very certain about the input for a full
circle. 'Look I should know, man . . . look round a circle . . . 360
innit . . . ?'

**By the end of the third session they had finished their direct
drive work and at this point they did define a procedure (Fig.
3.29). The pair had been so systematic about the recording that
there were no bugs in this procedure and they were delighted
with the final effect.**

Overview of Story

The local detail involved in this project was very important in terms
of turtle turn and distance estimation. Ravi and Shahidur used a full
range of angle inputs less than 180 and appeared to be making the
link between angle and turtle turn (compare with Sally and Janet's
work on angle described in Chapter 8). They were able to use and
reverse the ARCR command and in so doing came to appreciate the
units required for full, half and quarter circles. They were very
systematic about keeping their written record and combined all
possible commands before recording them on paper (apart from the
two ARCR commands). This project was not appropriate for the
introduction of ideas of subprocedure or variable although at a later
stage with different types of project they began to use these ideas.
The main feature of the Plane project was the concentration of the
pair, their motivation over a considerable period of time and their
attention to detail.

Fig. 3.29 The Completed Aeroplane

TO JET	BK 20	LT 95
LT 45	RT 90	RT 30
PU	FD 90	ARCR 5 90
BK 40	LT 80	ARCR 5 90
PD	FD 30	LT 20
FD 20	LT 70	FD 45
LT 35	FD 15	ARCL 5 90
ARCR 10 60	BK 15	LT 40
FD 40	RT 70	FD 50
LT 90	FD 5	RT 135
FD 20	RT 90	FD 5
RT 110	FD 5	RT 35
FD 5	RT 70	FD 60
RT 45	FD 5	LT 45
FD 20	LT 45	FD 60
BK 20	FD 15	RT 20
LT 45	BK 15	FD 30
FD 5	RT 45	ARCR 20 60
LT 110	FD 30	END

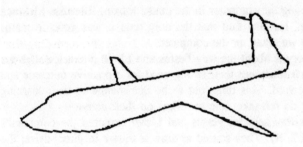

FESTUS AND LLOYD: WHIZZY EFFECTS

Festus and Lloyd were two first-year case study pupils. Festus was a quiet boy, confident and articulate. His mathematics teacher described Festus as a pupil who was well above average ability in maths. He believed, however, that Festus did not always fulfil his potential as he was easily distracted. Festus obviously worried about his work. He described one of the worst times he had in a maths lesson as being when 'We were scared we would get low marks and it was too quiet for me.' A fear of failure was evident in his Logo work which tended to be geared towards 'creating an end product', especially if this looked exciting. He said he had enjoyed

Logo and not found it difficult. The things he enjoyed best in his Logo work were 'Shapes like the squares and things.' He thought he had learned 'How to work the computer and it teaches you maths as well . . . Because you have to work out where to move . . . by the em degrees forward . . . ' When asked if he would want a computer in the maths lesson or not, Festus said he would want it "Cos we can get better at it . . . Thinking and working the computer . . . because it gives you more ideas how to work.'

Lloyd appeared to be lacking in confidence and was not very articulate. His first-year tutor described him as 'below average'. Similarly his maths teacher described Lloyd as a boy 'with limited ability', who found difficulty in concentrating for any length of time. Lloyd said that he enjoyed his maths lessons and was not aware of having any real difficulty with his work: 'I never had a bad time in maths.' This contrasted with his teacher's perception of his ability. When asked what he found most difficult Lloyd replied, 'Nothing really.' He said he enjoyed all his subjects. Lloyd had a computer at home, which he used mostly for games. He said he enjoyed using the computer in the maths lesson, 'Because I learned something.' He also said that the only time it was good in maths was when we 'Play on the computer.'

This story is about the way Festus and Lloyd interacted with the computer. It illustrates their strong need for a positive outcome and external reward. This turns out to be detrimental to their learning since they do not take time to reflect on their activity.

In their first session, Festus and Lloyd explored the commands FD, BK, LT, RT. They started to draw a square in direct drive; the first two sides looked reasonable but were not mathematically correct as the turtle turn was not 90. They then started again and produced a square using FD 90 RT 90 . . . They now used 90 for *all* inputs and did not distinguish distance from turn. They eventually typed a procedure for a square as follows:

Fig. 3.30 A Square Procedure

```
TO SQ
    FD 90
    RT 90
    FD 90
    RT 90
    FD 90
    RT 90
    FD 90
    END
```

The pair were constantly distracted by the work of other pairs and tended to try to copy procedures rather than construct them themselves. They even tried to copy the BACKGROUND command (which changes background colour), from another pair, although their screen was black and white! They also tried unsuccessfully to copy the REPEAT command from another pair.

In their second session, Festus and Lloyd managed to copy the syntax of the REPEAT command. They then made patterns using the REPEAT command such as:

```
REPEAT 30 [FD 20 RT 20]
```

and

```
REPEAT 25 [FD 10 RT 10]
```

They always used the same inputs to FD and RT and the number of REPEATS chosen was random. As they had no goal in view, they did not predict screen outcome nor reflect on the visual effect and its relationship with their commands.

They eventually defined a procedure for a circle:

```
TO CIRCLE
   REPEAT 23 [FD 20 RT 20]
   END
```

and rotated this to produce a pattern:

```
REPEAT 36 [CIRCLE RT 20]
```

Interestingly enough at this point Lloyd tried unsuccessfully to produce a triangle in direct drive. His work indicated that he had developed little understanding of turtle turn. **The pair soon became sidetracked by the rotating patterns being produced by another pair and returned to this activity themselves – it was more glamorous and safe.**

They eventually defined:

```
TO TWELVE
   REPEAT 12 [FD 30 RT 30]
   END
```

They then returned to direct mode to make a pattern for TWELVE by typing:

```
LT 30
TWELVE
LT 30
TWELVE
```

As the pattern emerged they commented on it. They were pleased but their comments did not exhibit any reflection on the structure of their pattern.

Lloyd 'It's good.'

Festus 'That's what I was trying to do.'

Lloyd 'You didn't know it was going to go like that.'

Festus 'I did know.'

Lloyd 'It's good innit Miss . . . Sir!'

Here Lloyd demonstrated his need for positive reinforcement. This was followed by an intervention to save the picture. This inadvertently emphasised the value of the end product.

Later the pair used the REPEAT command again to produce:

REPEAT 10 [TWELVE LT 30]

This did not produce a closed pattern but after trying out a range of numbers of REPEATS, the pair obtained what they wanted – that is REPEAT 12 [TWELVE LT 30].

Festus and Lloyd commenced the next session by looking over their procedures from the previous sessions. Festus wanted to draw something different, while Lloyd wanted to try a triangle – a goal which he had chosen in two previous sessions and had not persisted with and not yet completed successfully. They started by typing:

FD 30
RT 30
FD 30
RT 30

When they realised that this would produce the same as the procedure TWELVE written in the previous session, they abandoned the triangle goal and typed:

FD 50
RT 50
FD 50
RT 50

then:

REPEAT 7 [FD 50 RT 50]

which did not join up and:

REPEAT 7 [FD 40 RT 40]

which still did not join up; then:

REPEAT 9 [FD 40 RT 40]

which made a closed 9-sided shape, for which they defined a procedure KNIGHT:

Fig. 3.31 A Closed Shape

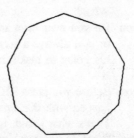

```
TO KNIGHT
    REPEAT 9 [FD 40 RT 40]
END
```

It is worth noting that all the inputs to FD and RT are the same. It seems very unlikely that the pair had a clear understanding at this stage of the meaning of FD and RT and the different effects the commands had on turtle state.

The pair then rotated KNIGHT around using the REPEAT command and eventually defined a procedure:

```
TO SUN
    REPEAT 36 [KNIGHT RT 55]
END
```

In their next session once again Festus and Lloyd started work without any discussion or negotiation of goal – they simply continued with their rotating patterns. Lloyd typed:

```
REPEAT 15 [FD 25 RT 25]
```

and then

```
REPEAT 10 [FD 40 RT 40]
```

The inputs to FD and RT were still always the same. They put this last REPEAT command into a procedure and then rotated it – exactly as in the previous sessions.

```
TO WELL
    REPEAT 10 [FD 40 RT 40]
END

REPEAT 50 [WELL RT 50]
```

The pretty pattern on the screen received praise:

Intervention 'Hey, that's great, it's absolutely amazing!'

We then tried to discover what the pair had understood in making their pattern and tried to provoke them to reflect on the processes in their procedure:

Intervention 'Do you know what it's going to do when you put the commands in?'

51

Festus   'What?'
Intervention 'Do you ever have any idea what it's going to do
                or is it always a surprise... ? Did you ever know
                it's going to make that sort of pattern?'
Festus   'No.'
Intervention 'Before you press RETURN what do you think will
                happen with that one?'
Festus   'That's what I said, just try and see what happens.'
Intervention 'What do you think might happen... Have you got
                any idea?'
Lloyd   'It might turn into a big ball.'
Intervention 'Let's have a look then.'
Lloyd   'Rubbish... Rubbish.'
Festus   'Let me do a nicer one.'

All through this session the pair continued to use the same inputs
to FD and RT and did not reflect upon their meaning nor indeed
even try BK or LT! The words simply had meaning in a syntactical
way – that is, as a formula to produce an interesting result. **There
was no connection made between the formalisation and the
structure of the visual effect.**

**In the next session, an intervention was made at the
beginning to try, first to direct the pair away from rotating
shapes and second to encourage the boys to discuss a goal
together** *before* **they started work on the computer. In trying to
draw a particular shape it was hoped that the boys would reach
an understanding of the meaning of FD and RT.**

Intervention 'What I would like you to do is to think of
                something that you can do together, something that
                you can draw or make.'
Festus   'What else apart from this stuff can we do?'

They thought that the only activity possible in Logo was drawing
rotated patterns!

Intervention 'You can do anything... what do you mean by
                "this stuff"?'
Festus   'I mean, um... apart from this section... does it
                have to be in this section?'
Intervention 'Well, I mean instead of doing patterns and circles
                and things you might decide to draw a car or a boat
                or something like that.'
Festus   'How are we going to draw that?'

Intervention 'Well . . . that's up to you to work out . . . you could try it out first, write down the commands that work and then do a program for that afterwards . . . Do you see what I mean? . . . If you keep a record of everything you do, then when you know it works you can make a program for it.'

They had great difficulty in deciding on a goal and after a while:

Festus 'Miss, this is difficult . . . we don't know what to do . . . '

They decided in the end to draw a 'break dancer'. They adopted a strategy of direct driving and recording commands. Festus was a champion break dancer and so they felt quite motivated to draw this image on the screen. They also did not feel it was a step backwards as they still received praise for their work from their peers because of Festus's prowess in the dancing field! The pair were faced for the first time with a situation where they had to sort out the meanings and effects of distance and turn in Logo and how, if mistakes were made in their recording, they could debug using the visual feedback from the screen for assistance.

Overview of Story

Festus and Lloyd had a strong need for a positive outcome. They initially achieved this by copying a rotated pattern procedure from another pair. Having copied this at an early stage they continued to produce rotated patterns unless other goals were introduced. The value of the end product was unwittingly emphasised by the teacher on numerous occasions by her praise of the beauty of the patterns. Festus and Lloyd's work shows that they did not initially understand the use of the REPEAT command nor the definition of procedure. They were inhibited from trying to understand them because of their need to produce impressive patterns.

By the end of their fourth session a consistent structure within which the pair used REPEAT and procedures for rotated patterns had emerged. This was:

- Make a shape, which is 'closed but overlapping'
- Define a procedure for this, usually in the form:

```
TO SHAPE
  REPEAT Y [FD X RT X]
  END
```

where Y and X are any natural numbers.

- Rotate the shape using the structure
  REPEAT A [SHAPE RT B]
  where A and B are any natural numbers.

This was a framework which for them produced success! They did not really see that there were other possibilities for Logo use.

Festus and Lloyd's activity throughout the year highlights the detrimental effect of copying. The pair did not understand the processes involved in the use of the REPEAT command or in procedure definition because they had not constructed these ideas themselves. They were then loathe to move on to anything else as the 'gaps' in their knowledge would quickly become apparent. Only when they were jolted out of this mode and embarked on a specific 'drawing project' were they able to begin to make sense of the primitives of Logo.

NOTE

1 State-transparent procedure in turtle graphics is one in which the turtle orientation and position is the same at the beginning and end of the procedure.

4

Problem Solving

PROBLEM SOLVING AND MATHEMATICS

One of the aims of the Logo Maths Project was to investigate the
problem-solving strategies used by pupils in the Logo programming
environment. Problem solving is important in mathematics
education as pointed out in the influential Cockcroft Report
(Cockcroft, 1982), 'The ability to solve problems is at the heart of
mathematics' (para. 249, p. 73). It is generally accepted that
mathematics education is not only about concepts and skills but
also concerns the processes by which these concepts and skills are
learnt and applied in a variety of situations. This is by no means
something peculiar to mathematics as mentioned by Bruner (1966):
'... a theory of instruction seeks to take account of the fact that a
curriculum reflects not only the nature of knowledge itself but also,
the nature of the knower and the knowledge getting process ...
knowing is a process not a product' (p. 72).

There is now a considerable body of research literature about
this topic which ranges from the identification of heuristic processes
to discussion of how problem-solving strategies are learnt and
improved. Much of the work on problem solving makes reference
to Polya's (1945) four phases in problem-solving activity, namely:
understanding the problem, devising a plan, carrying out the plan,
and looking back. These have been developed in the UK by, for
example, Mason, Burton and Stacey (1982) who identified the
processes of specialising, conjecturing, generalising and convincing
which they suggest operate along spiral loops – each loop building
upon the understandings developed through transversing through
the previous loops. There has been, however, only limited success
with programs that teach general heuristics. As Kilpatrick (1985)

points out in his review of twenty-five years of research on problem solving, 'Researchers have had some success in getting students to use heuristic procedures when the procedures have been explained, illustrated, and practised. They have had much more difficulty getting an improvement in the number of problems solved correctly' (Kilpatrick, 1985, p. 11). Schoenfeld made a similar point though even more negatively, 'in spite of the large number of hours that our students spend in the study of mathematics – and that includes time spent studying "problem solving" – they may be seeing, and learning, nearly nothing about thinking mathematically' (Schoenfeld, 1982, p. 363).

Increasingly, attention has been paid to classroom climate and the need to encourage pupils to move from a product-orientated approach which is concerned only with a superficial involvement with the problem to one that is more reflective and demands effort and time commitment. This implies a shift in the didactical relations in the mathematics class and a move to more pupil autonomy and responsibility – where pupils are actively involved in the construction of their own knowledge and make their own decisions as to strategy and explanation. In line with this trend, there has been a greater emphasis on the employment of peer group interaction as a vehicle for developing problem-solving skills through the articulation of one's own plans and explaining and arguing with others.

Many researchers have also pointed to the key role of metacognition, 'thinking about one's own thinking', in the problem-solving process (see, for example, Schoenfeld, 1985). The control aspect of metacognition relates to decisions about choice of strategy, organisation and sequencing, implementation and evaluation. This self-regulation is itself influenced by the metacognitive knowledge one holds about oneself, one's preferred working style and perceived competence.

Researchers are also now acknowledging the crucial significance of an appropriate structural knowledge base to problems and the contextual influences on problem-solving strategies in the ways that particular contexts 'call up' specific problem-solving approaches. This is aptly summarised in the following quotation from Lave et al. (1984): 'In didactical terms, people and settings together create problems and solution shapes, and moreover, they do so simultaneously. Very often a process of solution occurs in the setting, with the enactment of the problem, and may transform the problem for the solver. Indeed, activity-setting relations are integral, generative and finally dialectical in nature' (Lave *et al.*, 1984, p. 94). There is now less emphasis – at least among some researchers – on the acquisition of *general* problem-solving heuristics and even a scepticism as to their existence. As Minsky states, 'You must... be particularly wary of methods you can *always* use – such methods are *too* general, they're things that one can always do, but they do not apply especially well, to any particular problem – it isn't any accident that things we can "always" do are just the ones we should rarely do' (his emphasis) (Minsky, 1986, p. 145).

Finally, we would also wish to point to the importance, in our view, of problem posing – that is the activity of problem generation – both of itself and because of its close relationship with problem solving. As Brown and Walter (1983) state, '... the act of problem solving requires some reformulation of the original problem that is essentially a problem generating activity' (Brown and Walter, 1983, p. 122).

To summarise the arguments, we suggest that any problem will be easier to solve the more one knows about the context in which the problem is situated, rather than the more one knows about decontextualised problem-solving strategies. It would seem that problem-solving strategies are largely tailored by the expectations of the problem solver within a particular setting – *but* it is confidence in this setting which can be built upon in other settings.

PROBLEM SOLVING AND LOGO

The investigation of problem-solving strategies within a particular setting – that of Logo-based work – very clearly is in line with the above brief review. It also raises the whole question of metacognition – that is, how far it is true that the programming activity and the visual outcomes on the screen allow pupils to externalise their own thinking and reflect upon it.

There has already been some investigation of the ways in which the mathematical and heuristic processes of primary schoolchildren develop as they learn to program in Logo (Noss, 1985). Noss's approach is similar to that of the Logo Maths Project in that it takes as a premise that mathematical thinking is something we do all the time in making sense of our world and that Logo is an environment in which heuristic and conceptual ideas of mathematics are embedded. Enough is not yet known about the individual nature of problem-solving strategies used by pupils when programming. Research which expects some sort of 'idealised' problem-solving skill to transfer from programming to other contexts appears to us to be rather naive in its approach (see, for example, Pea and Kurland (1984)). Clements (1986), however, carried out an experiment to assess the effect of learning programming and computer-assisted learning on specific cognitive skills (for example, reflectivity, divergent thinking) and concluded that 'Logo programming can increase performance in specific cognitive and metacognitive skills and on measures of creativity' (Clements, 1986, p. 317).

At the core of a problem-solving environment designed around interactive work with a computer are the processes of conjecturing, trying out and debugging – as evidenced in the case studies described in Chapter 3. The fact that errors can become 'bugs' in a Logo environment – that is something to learn from – is crucially important in encouraging an investigative approach. The formalisation required by the programming language is also fundamental to the problem-solving process. It provides a 'bridge' between the pupils' actions and their understanding of general mathematical relationships since the requirement to write a program 'forces' pupils to capture their understandings in symbolic form and thus clarify them (see, for example, the case study of George and Asim, Chapter 3).

Problem posing can also arise quite naturally in a Logo environment. At the beginning of the Logo Maths Project the case study pupils were given the freedom to choose their own goals and develop their own problem-solving and programming strategies. In this way they developed confidence in their computer interactions and discovered what the computer could and could not do. We found that pupils, working in pairs, had no difficulty in coming up with ideas to investigate. Our role was to facilitate discussion, encourage questioning, pose additional challenges and generally try to orientate the pupils to think about their activities and reflect upon the relationship between their actions and the computer feedback. Although our interventions were focused on process – in the form of encouraging the pupils to reflect – we did not impose on the pupils or try to teach them any 'idealised' problem-solving strategies.

TYPES OF PROGRAMMING ACTIVITY

We have identified the following three broad categories of programming activity in a Logo environment.

Working at a Syntactical Level

This activity consists of the syntactically correct use of Logo primitives, procedures (or sequences of these) but with a focus on obtaining a screen output without any apparent reflection of how or why the output was achieved. Examples of such activity are random typing of commands, passively 'copying' from other pupils or from a handbook or randomly putting inputs into the REPEAT command. Our observations have led us to believe that pupils who work at a syntactical level are not necessarily provoked to think about the processes involved in their work (see, for example, the case study of Festus and Lloyd, Chapter 3). The immediate feedback from the screen can sometimes encourage pupils to work in this way – particularly when the classroom climate is competitive and product oriented. We would suggest that teacher intervention is necessary if this sort of programming activity is observed and a specific goal or project suggested or a challenge set.

'Making Sense Of'

This is exploratory activity in which pupils try out a new idea or procedure and reflect on what is happening. Sometimes such activity is completely non-goal directed, sometimes it takes place within goal-directed activity and sometimes a goal emerges from the activity (see, for example, the case study of Sally and Janet, Chapter 3). 'Making sense of' activity exploits the interactive power of Logo as a medium for moving through the learning spiral: conjecture, test, debug. If pupils are to develop an understanding of the processes involved in Logo programming we would suggest that it is important that pupils are encouraged to explore in this way and 'take time out' from working towards predefined goals.

Goal-directed Activity

This is activity aimed at achieving a specific goal which may be posed by the teacher or pupil. The projects described in Chapter 3 contain some examples of some goal-directed activity. For completeness we give here two more illustrations.

The Butterfly

Fig. 4.1 George and Asim: The Butterfly

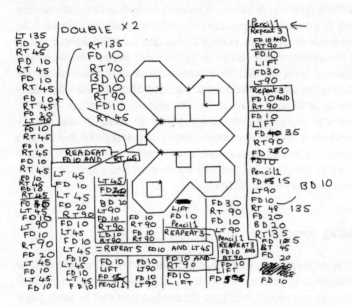

Throughout their first year of learning Logo, George and Asim always chose for themselves picture goals. They preplanned their work very carefully, usually away from the computer. Their planning took the form of drawing out their design on graph paper, writing a linear sequence of commands and only splitting these into subprocedures when this was imposed by the storage restrictions of the machine (see, for example, Fig. 4.1).

The Prison

Sally and Janet were asked to draw a pattern of squares (Fig. 4.2). Before they worked on the computer the pair saw the task as consisting of four outer squares and four connected inner squares. They therefore defined a square module which initially was state transparent. They then tried out this square module and decided to delete the last command (see Fig 4.2) so that the four outer squares could be produced merely by typing SQUARE SQUARE SQUARE SQUARE (note the similarity of the way of working to that in the construction of the design of STARBUSTER, Chapter 3). They put these four procedures into a superprocedure PRISON, then simply added a string of commands for the inner 'square'. The act of making a written record of these commands led the pair to notice that the commands made a square, to then 'see' the inner square and finally use their SQUARE procedure again for the inner square by adding an appropriate interface command (LT 90) as illustrated in Fig. 4.2 below.

Fig. 4.2 Sally and Janet: The Prison

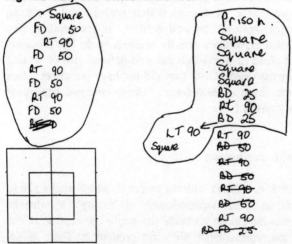

We have distinguished two separate dimensions along which turtle graphics goals can be classified:

(a) Loosely defined . . . Well defined
(b) Real world . . . Abstract

Our data suggests that the 'position' of the goal with respect to these two dimensions affects both pupil interaction and behaviour.

(a) Loosely Defined ... Well Defined

This dimension is concerned with the extent to which pupils have articulated and planned the final outcome of their work. On the one hand, loosely-defined goals are characterised by a lack of detailed preplanned structure; they evolve out of exploratory 'making sense of' activity (for example, the STARBUSTER project in Chapter 3). Well-defined goals on the other hand have a well worked out overall structure and global product – the structure arising from detailed preplanning by the pupils or from the embedded mathematical relationships. (The Butterfly is an example of a well-defined goal with attributes arising from real world representations, and the Prison described above is an example of a well-defined goal whose structure is organised by the mathematical attributes of the shapes.)

Because of the modular structure of Logo we have found it necessary to separate out global from local structure. The global 'looseness' of the goal does not imply that a local subgoal is not tightly structured by the pupils – the STARBUSTER project illustrates a loosely-defined goal with well-defined local modules. In a similar way, at a local level within well-defined goals, an individual module may *not* be well defined; its composition may emerge from local exploratory activity in direct mode. For example, when a pair of children worked on the well-defined goal of writing a procedure for the word LONG they did not have prescribed plans for defining the shape of each letter ... these emerged from their activity at the keyboard.

(b) Real World ... Abstract

This dimension is concerned with the extent to which pupils aim to come up with an actual representation of 'reality'. It must be stressed that this dimension concerns the pupils' perception of the 'realness' of the representation they are producing. There is not necessarily anything objectively more real about the image of a flower than an image of a square but we have found that pupils' programming style is influenced by how they *see* the image they are drawing; that is, whether they see it as a picture of something in their 'real world' or whether they see it as an abstract pattern. In the case study of 'The Spiral' in Chapter 3, a dispute arose between George and Asim as to how far they saw their Spiral – as a representation of the picture or simply as a shape constructed by a sequence of mathematical relations.

Figure 4.3 illustrates some pupil goals classified according to the above dimensions.

Fig. 4.3 Classification of Pupil Goals

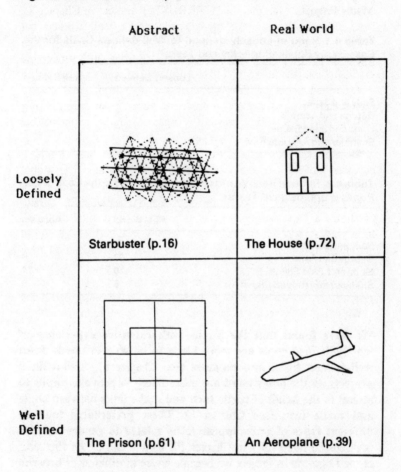

	Abstract	Real World
Loosely Defined	Starbuster (p.16)	The House (p.72)
Well Defined	The Prison (p.61)	An Aeroplane (p.39)

CHOICE OF GOALS

When pupils are given the freedom to choose their own goals they exhibit preferences for certain types of projects. This is illustrated in the following table which summarises the goals chosen by the longitudinal case study pupils during the three years of the Logo Maths Project.

Table 4.1 Ratio of Loosely-defined to Well-defined Goals for the Case Study Pupils (Pupil-devised Tasks)

	Loosely Defined	Well Defined
Sally and Janet	16	4
George and Asim	5	18
Linda and Jude/Elaine	16	8
Shahidur and Amanda/Ravi	0	6

Table 4.2 Ratio of Real-World to Abstract Goals for the Case Study Pupils (Pupil-devised Tasks)

	Real World	Abstract
Sally and Janet	11	7
George and Asim	23	0
Linda and Jude/Elaine	10	14
Shahidur and Amanda/Ravi	6	0

We have found that the pupils with extensive experience of loosely-defined goals are more likely to be able to break down well-defined tasks into modules (see Chapter 5). Well-defined projects on the other hand are more likely to provoke pupils to attend to the detail of turtle turn and make links between angle and turtle turn (see Chapter 8). These preferences towards different types of goals appear to be related to gender and this is discussed more fully in Chapter 10. By the end of the first year of the Logo Maths Project we became aware of differences between pupils in their choice of goals and the consequences for their learning. We therefore gave tasks to encourage pupils to choose different types of work.

PROGRAMMING STYLE

We found that the way pupils worked with Logo depended on their expectations, their perception of the goal in terms of the two dimensions described earlier, the classroom climate and, finally, personal preference in working style – itself evidently influenced by emotional factors such as confidence.

Within goal-directed work, we have identified different subsets of activity: planning, implementing and debugging, all of which can have either a local or a global focus. Local activity focuses on the immediate graphics or text output; while global activity focuses on the overall picture or mental plan. These processes together with their interaction with the negotiation of a goal, are represented in Fig. 4.4.

Fig 4.4 Type of Programming Activity

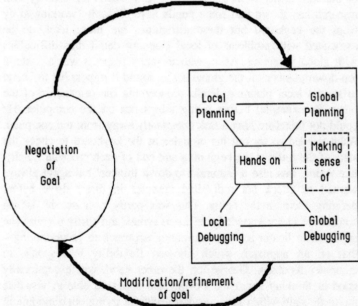

We suggest that the *sequence* in which these activities are carried out depends on a pupil's individual programming style as well as the context and nature of the problem. A pupil's programming style varies along the following dimensions:

| Top-down planning.............................Bottom-up planning |
| Attention to global.............................Attention to local |
| characteristics   characteristics |
| Preference for working in the.............Preference for working in |
| editor before testing out in   direct drive before working |
| direct drive   in editor |

The dimension 'top-down', 'bottom-up' is discussed in Chapter 5. The other two dimensions are described in relation to planning and debugging.

Planning

If we recognise the existence of differences in programming style, it would seem important to allow pupils to find their own balance of planning away from the computer and 'hands-on' activity. Our research has shown that some pupils have difficulty working away from the keyboard but these difficulties are more likely to be associated with problems of local planning detail than difficulties with global planning. Asim, who in many respects was a 'natural top-down planner' in the global sense, found it impossible to attend to all the local planning details (concerning the orientation of the turtle for example) before trying things out on the computer. He could not therefore *plan* a task *completely* away from the computer. Asim needed to try out his modules at the keyboard to check the state of the turtle at the beginning and end of each procedure. Sally, like Asim, was also a 'natural top-down thinker' but again always wanted to check her individual modules in direct drive before defining them in the editor. This was partly because she lacked confidence in her knowledge of Logo syntax and partly because she appeared to favour a more negotiating approach to programming – that is, an approach which allowed flexibility in response to computer feedback. George, on the other hand, was exceptionally good at thinking about local detail and appeared able to visualise the turtle state within his procedures without trying out a module in direct drive. This meant that George was able to plan away from the computer, and he preferred to work in this way. Although he planned away from the computer he did not necessarily analyse the problem in a structured manner. It was in fact only after considerable teacher intervention that George began to use a modular structure in the design of his programs. This is discussed in more detail in Chapter 5. What is ultimately required is a synthesis of planning, at both a local and global level, with the 'hands-on' work.

Debugging

Debugging similarly can be approached locally or globally. Some pupils debugged simply by focusing on each command in turn and checking sequentially, while other pupils would 'trap' the bug by 'seeing' where the program had gone wrong. In pupils' early work we have identified phases in the way errors are tackled. After initial unsystematic work, pupils learnt to keep a record of their commands and when faced with bugs check the procedure commands in turn with their written record. This is at first done without reference to visual outcome on the screen and without appreciation of how reflection on this visual outcome might help in tracking down the error. This is illustrated in the following short extracts.

John and Panos

John and Panos had drawn a rocket but had introduced an incorrect command into their procedure. John said, 'Right, now where was it we went wrong?' After checking each command in turn, Panos exclaimed, pointing at his paper and the screen editor for emphasis: 'RT 20 ... it ain't got no RT 20 ... that's where it went wrong.'

Later in the session, however, John applied a more global debugging strategy by reference to the visual image of the 'buggy' rocket on the screen: '... Look, Panos – the line's crossed ... so it's this that's wrong ... it's LT 110 that's wrong.'

Sally and Janet

In the third year of the project Sally and Janet had constructed a procedure 'BFLY' for a butterfly (see Fig. 4.5) which called two triangular subprocedures for the wings. Their strategy for navigating between each module was to centre (CT) the turtle before each call of triangle and before drawing each antenna.

67

Fig. 4.5: Sally and Janet: The Butterfly

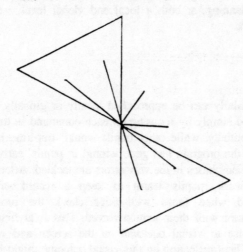

They tried out their BFLY program and there was a bug. Sally said, 'Oh, that one went wrong.' Looking at the screen Sally went on to comment: 'We probably forgot to put centre ... you know what probably happened ... there should be four centres shouldn't there, 'cos each time we centred it. If I forgot to put one down ... '

The pair did not try to find the missing CT, by reference to the screen, but adopted a local debugging approach by 'walking' step by step through the BFLY procedure.

Later, of course, their use of centre to navigate between modules caused problems when they wanted to draw butterflies all over the screen! The pair had moved the turtle away from the centre and confidently typed BFLY when the following interaction took place. Sally: 'There is something wrong with it. What went wrong?' Sally's first conjecture was that the size was causing the problem. She said, 'It's because it's too small.'

After an intervention suggesting that they reflect on what the turtle had done, Janet commented: 'Oh, it went to CT and we're not in the centre.' The pair then 'saw' how they could debug. Janet said 'Take it to the middle of the butterfly each time.'

This second example illustrates the two approaches to debugging and also shows how negotiation of a new goal – here from one butterfly to several – can interrelate planning with debugging approaches in an effective way. **The global trapping of the bug in the extended goal, we suggest, was only possible because of the**

careful way the strategy had been devised and debugged locally within the initial goal.

IMPLICATIONS FOR CLASSROOM PRACTICE

We have identified a variety of pupil approaches to Logo programming both in choice of goal and in ways of working in order to achieve a goal. We believe that the role of the teacher should be to help pupils become aware of *all* that is available in the Logo environment by posing different types of goals and encouraging flexibility in problem-solving approaches to programming – that is, in planning, experimenting and debugging. This can be done in a number of ways. The pupil who naturally prefers to define procedures in the editor needs to know when it is appropriate to try out modules in direct drive, while the pupil who always works in direct drive needs to be shown the power of defining in the editor and provoked to predict the output of procedures before they are run. The pupil who preplans work in a very detailed way at a local level needs to be encouraged to exploit the investigative environment provided by Logo, while the pupil who simply interacts with the computer in an unreflective syntactic way needs to be invited to plan, predict and reflect on the outcomes of the computer interactions.

There cannot be and should not be hard and fast rules for teacher practice in relation to problem solving in Logo. Our findings do indicate, however, that asking pupils to plan a project away from the computer can be unnecessarily and unnaturally restrictive. We also suggest that different representations of a task can provide a useful intermediate step towards program design or debugging – for example, creating a written record or 'playing turtle'. Perhaps the most important point to take away from this chapter is an acceptance of the *value* of variety in approach and sequence and that no one way can ever be 'optimal' for all pupils.

5

Subprocedure and Modularity

BACKGROUND

One of the most important features of Logo is its procedural nature. It is not unreasonable therefore to suppose that using Logo as a programming environment will encourage pupils to use modularity; that is procedures as building blocks within the design of their computer programs. It has also been assumed that using Logo will facilitate the design of structured programs; that is, programs which have been developed in a 'top-down' hierarchical manner. A simple example of 'top-down' design is as follows:

Suppose in order to write a program to draw the picture of the face, we approached the problem by first writing down the following Logo program:

Fig. 5.1 Example of 'Top-down' Design

```
TO  FACE
      OUTLINE
      MOVE1
      EYE
      MOVE2
      EYE
      MOVE3
      MOUTH
      END
```

We have structured the problem into one of writing subprocedures to draw the outline of the face, the mouth and the eyes. We have decided to use the same subprocedure or module for each eye. We have also decided that we will need three navigating modules, MOVE1, MOVE2 and MOVE3. At the stage of writing down the FACE superprocedure we are not concerned with the details of the subprocedures – these are worked out after we have made our 'top-down' plan. A 'top-down' approach therefore implies that the programmer has analysed the problem in a structured manner away from the computer and translated this analysis into a set of procedures in a realistic way.

Harvey (1985) points out that 'according to structured programming, you should never have to do any debugging. You should start with a complete, clear program specification' (Harvey, 1985, p. 171). He stresses that this approach is alien to the Logo philosophy, in which debugging and modification are activities which are made accessible by the interactive nature of the language. He goes on to point out that, 'One area of computer science in which the top-down approach has not been accepted so enthusiastically is artificial intelligence. All researchers try to program computers to carry out ill-defined, complex tasks (playing chess is a prototypical example) for which there is no single, obvious method. In that kind of research project you can't start by writing down on paper a complete specification of how the project will be organised. Instead you start with a more or less vague idea, you try programming it, and then you play around with it to try to improve the results' (Harvey, 1985, p. 165). Logo is derived from the artificial intelligence language, Lisp, so Harvey suggests that, in a Logo environment, programmers also tend to work in a more 'bottom-up' programming style.

For the simple task of writing a procedure to draw a face, 'bottom-up' programming might mean working on the eyes and the mouth *before* linking them together as a whole. A 'bottom-up' approach tends to imply more interaction and negotiation with the computer, during which procedures may or may not be used and interfaces may not be well defined.

Some studies have addressed the issue of whether or not pupils are able to use procedures and modularity in Logo. Leron (1983) reported that 'most six-graders (12-year-olds) I have seen tend to write long, step by step, unstructured procedures. Moreover, even when explicitly prompted to use subprocedures they seem to "resist" the suggestion and return to their "linear" style as soon as they are left alone' (Leron, 1983, p. 348). He related these pupil difficulties to their 'lack of a clear concept of the interface between any two subprocedures, and the related importance of the turtle state before and after each subprocedure' (Leron, 1983, p. 348). More recently Hillel and Samurçay reported that 'despite the fact that our children have been provided with extensive experience of

71

procedures and the fact that we have discussed the relative merits of using procedures, they surprisingly often opt for writing simple programs (i.e. using only Logo primitives). I think that a plausible explanation for this is the overwhelming identification by the children as 'drawing with the turtle' (Hillel and Samurçay, 1985).

Although we would go along to some extent with both these observations and their interpretation, our work suggests that there are factors which should be taken into account other than those mentioned above. Harvey suggests a 'top-down' or 'bottom-up' programming style can be influenced by the type of programming problem, and we support this view. This chapter will discuss the factors which we found to influence pupils' choice firstly as to whether or not to use subprocedures and modularity in their program design and secondly whether or not to program in a 'top-down' or 'bottom-up' manner.

GOALS AND STRUCTURED PROGRAMMING

We described in Chapter 4 how after the first year of our Project, it was possible to categorise pupil goals along the following dimensions:

Loosely defined . . . Well defined
Real world . . . Abstract

We found that the type of goal in which the pupils engaged influenced whether or not they chose to use subprocedures and modularity in their program design. The rest of this section will illustrate this claim by reference to examples defined in terms of these dimensions.

Loosely-defined, Real-world Goals

For many pupils, Logo programming activity begins with the production of a real-world image (e.g. a house, a flower, a dog or a ship) in which the writing of a procedure is seen as a way of describing and then saving the image on the screen. Some of these real-world goals are loosely defined. The way pupils approach such goals is illustrated in the work of Sally and Janet.

Sally and Janet developed a strategy of building up their real-world images on the screen with no clearly defined 'a priori' idea of the eventual outcome. In the beginning stages of this way of working they kept a record of their direct drive commands and when they had completed their project divided this record up into sequential parts – each part representing a functional element of the design (e.g. a window, a door, a roof). They then defined a subprocedure for each of these functional parts. They developed this approach so that a new subprocedure was written immediately after a new part of the design had been completed in direct mode. This new subprocedure would then be simply added to the superprocedure in the editor. Defining subprocedures in this way was a useful tool for the pupils since once they had defined and added to the superprocedure, the image, as far as it had been constructed, could be immediately reproduced without typing in the commands again. Subprocedures were, however, merely seen as a way of saving commands as illustrated by the following comment from Janet: 'We can do this procedure now . . . it's much easier to do it that way than typing the whole bloody lot in.'

The final superprocedure MAD (Fig. 5.2) was quite typical of the procedures produced by pupils working towards loosely-defined 'real-world' goals. The subprocedures consisted of the commands for the 'picture' of the functional element together with the commands for 'navigation' between pictures – so they were in no sense reusable modules.

It is important to recognise that the motivation for Sally and Janet's program design did not arise from a 'top-down' plan. It can be traced to two external influences – the system with which they worked which would not accept long procedures and a very specific intervention: 'I'd like you to write some separate procedures for different parts.'

Throughout their first year of Logo programming Sally and Janet always worked in this sequential manner when drawing a representation of the real world. They did not analyse the image into constituent parts. This is quite reasonable given that there would have been little pay-off for them to work in this way in terms of achieving their objectives at that particular time. However, it appears that this pragmatic need for economy of action served as a basis for future development in perceiving patterns within a programming task. In fact Sally and Janet used the strategy of dividing up a written record into parts even when working on more well-defined goals and this approach eventually seemed to help them perceive modularity within a well-defined design.

73

Fig. 5.2 The House

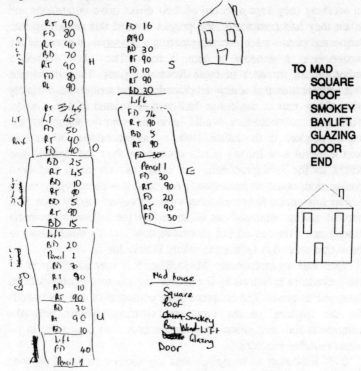

TO MAD
SQUARE
ROOF
SMOKEY
BAYLIFT
GLAZING
DOOR
END

TO SQUARE	TO ROOF	TO BAYLIFT	TO GLAZING	TO DOOR
RT 90	LT 45	PU	PU	PU
FD 80	FD 50	BK 20	FD 40	FD 74
RT 90	RT 90	PD	PD	RT 90
BK 70	FD 50	BK 30	FD 10	BK 5
RT 90	END	RT 90	RT 90	RT 90
FD 80		BK 10	BK 30	PD
RT 90	TO SMOKEY	BK 30	RT 90	FD 30
BK 70	BK 25	RT 90	FD 10	RT 90
END	RT 45	RT 90	END	FD 10
	BK 10	FD 10		RT 90
	RT 90	RT 90		FD 30
	BK 5	BK 30		END
	RT 90	END		
	BK 15			
	END			

Loosely-defined, Abstract Goals

In the beginning stages of learning Logo many pupils choose to define a procedure for a regular polygon – usually a square. This procedure is almost always non-state transparent as a complete image on the screen is obtained without turning the turtle to its original orientation. Pupils soon discover that when they repeatedly enter the procedure name a rotated pattern is produced (Fig. 5.3). If at this point there is a teacher intervention to show pupils how to define a superprocedure for the new shape, pupils will tend to consolidate this strategy – that is, they will continue to define a procedure for an abstract image and then use it to build up a new goal in a loosely-defined way.

The procedural nature of Logo within the turtle graphics subset encourages this creative building-up activity. The final program can consist of many layers of nested subprocedures which evolve during the 'hands-on' computer activity. Analysis of the pupils' use of subprocedure throughout the three years of our study indicates that using subprocedures in the context of building up to loosely-defined abstract goals has an important influence on pupils' developing ability to analyse a well-defined goal into parts and using subprocedures to represent these parts.

Fig. 5.3 Rotated Pattern of Squares

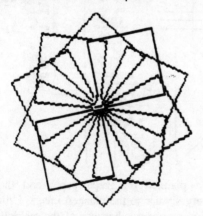

Well-defined, Real-world Goals

Pupils who choose well-defined real-world goals (as described in detail in Chapter 4) tend to focus more on the detail of their design than on the structure of their program. This focus on the precision of the whole object makes it less likely that they will take on the idea of dividing their commands into subprocedures. George and Asim, for example, always chose for themselves well-defined real-world goals during their first year of Logo and learned less about the ideas of subprocedure during this year than, for example, Sally and Janet who had always chosen either loosely-defined real-world goals or loosely-defined abstract goals. An example of one of George and Asim's well-defined real-world goals is presented in Fig. 5.4.

Fig. 5.4 The Rabbit

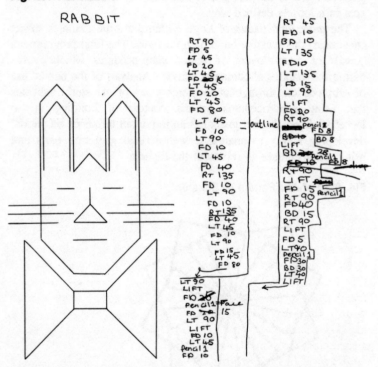

This picture had been planned on graph paper and the final computer image was very similar to the planned image. Ultimately the pair had to write two procedures because of the restrictions of the space of the computer system, but they did not attempt to join these two procedures into a superprocedure and the two subprocedures were in no way related to the separate 'parts' of the rabbit's head.

Well-defined, Abstract Goals

We suggest that it is only when pupils are working towards a well-defined abstract goal that they begin to perceive a need to break down their program into subprocedures or modules at the beginning of a project in a top-down way. An example of this type of project is given by the star shape in Fig. 5.5, and an approach with respect to this type of goal is illustrated in the work of Beverley and Tina, two of the first-year case study pupils.

Fig. 5.5 The Star

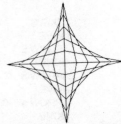

Beverley and Tina brought a 'paper and pencil' drawing of the star shape to their eighth Logo session. There was no doubt that they wanted to reproduce the image *exactly* – in other words this was, for them, a well-defined goal. They first of all drew a cross (for the axes) and then decided to fill in the top left-hand quadrant. They saw this as a module which could then be reused in each quadrant. Thus they had a top-down plan which consisted of four calls of the same subprocedure together with appropriate interfaces. After considerable trial and error they drew the left-hand quadrant in direct drive and then defined a procedure for the pattern which they called STAR. They then worked out together how to fit the four STARs together to make their star shape. They were able to do this since they had spent many previous sessions building up loosely-defined images using a defined procedure and then defining a superprocedure for the final outcome.

Teacher-devised Tasks

When we realised, after analysing the data from the first year of the study, that well-defined abstract goals were more likely to provoke pupils to need to use subprocedure and modularity we introduced a range of 'teacher-devised' tasks. Several of these tasks were

77

associated with the idea of using variable – an idea which is ultimately linked to the construction of general modules. An example of one of these tasks is the 'Row of Pines' task (Fig. 5.6a). This task was given to all the case study pupils after they had undertaken approximately 40 hours of 'hands-on' Logo experience.

An example of one of the programs written by Shahidur and Ravi is given in Fig. 5.6b below. As can be seen from this program the pair used both subprocedures and modularity in their solution of this task.

Fig. 5.6 The 'Row of Pines' Task

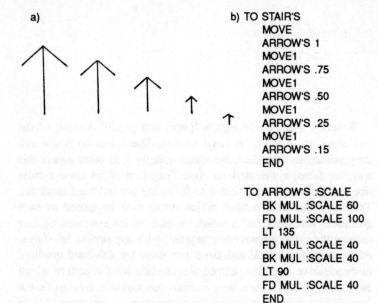

a)

b) TO STAIR'S
   MOVE
   ARROW'S 1
   MOVE1
   ARROW'S .75
   MOVE1
   ARROW'S .50
   MOVE1
   ARROW'S .25
   MOVE1
   ARROW'S .15
   END

TO ARROW'S :SCALE
   BK MUL :SCALE 60
   FD MUL :SCALE 100
   LT 135
   FD MUL :SCALE 40
   BK MUL :SCALE 40
   LT 90
   FD MUL :SCALE 40
   END

All of the pupils in solving the 'Row of Pines' task defined a general module for the 'pine tree', a separate startup procedure and separate 'navigating' procedures. We suggest that this common approach was adopted since it was self-evidently functional in this particular setting.

PUPILS USING SUBPROCEDURE AND MODULARITY

At the end of each year of the Logo Maths Project all the longitudinal case study pupils were given a specific task, the 'Four Squares' task (Fig. 5.7) to be undertaken individually in the university computer laboratory. The task was designed to probe how pupils saw the task, how their programs reflected these perceptions and whether in particular the ideas of subprocedure and modularity were used. We were also interested in tracing changes in approach over the three years of the research. This task was also given to the extended network pupils at the end of the first and second year of the extended network study.

Fig. 5.7 The 'Four Squares' Task

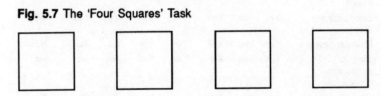

Table 5.1 presents an overview of the case study pupils' solutions to the 'Four Squares' task at the end of each year of the longitudinal study. It shows that by the end of three years all the children exhibited a good grasp of modular design, although they did not necessarily separate navigation from drawing commands.

Sally's procedure for the 'Four Squares' task at the end of the first year of the longitudinal study is presented in Fig 5.8a. This should be contrasted with George's solution (Fig. 5.8b). Sally used subprocedures in her solution. The nature of George's solution indicates that George, with assistance, could probably have used subprocedures since there is evidence of structure in his sequential list of commands. During the preceding year Sally had used the idea of subprocedure in 13 out of her 15 projects and George had used subprocedure in 7 out of his 16 projects. This was predominantly due to the nature of the goals towards which they had chosen to work.

Table 5.1 Overview of Case Study Pupils' Solutions to the 'Four Squares' Task at the end of each Year of Study

	Sally	Asim	George	Janet	Jude	Ravi	Linda	Shahidur
Year 1								
Clear Global Plan[1]	Yes	Yes	Yes	Yes	Yes	—	Yes	—
Modular design[2]	Yes	Yes	No	Yes	No	—	Yes	—
Startup commands sep. subpro.[3]	Yes	No	No	Yes	No	—	No	—
Navigating commands sep. module[4]	No	No	No	No	No	—	No	—
Year 2								
Clear Global Plan	Yes	Yes	Yes	Yes	Yes	Yes	Yes	Yes
Modular design	Yes	Yes	Yes	Yes	Yes	No	Yes	No
Startup commands sep.subpro.	Yes	Yes	No	Yes	No	No	No	No
Navigating commands sep. module	Yes	No	No	No	No	No	No	No
Year 3								
Clear Global Plan	Yes	Yes	Yes	Yes	Yes	Yes	Yes	Yes
Modular design	Yes	Yes	Yes	Yes	Yes	Yes	Yes	Yes
Startup commands sep. subpro.	Yes	Yes	Yes	Yes	Yes	No	No	No
Navigating commands sep. module	No	No	No	Yes	No	No	No	No

1. Clear Global Plan: Evidence of structure in sequential commands although no modular subprocedures used (see Fig.5.8b).
2. Modular Design: Modular subprocedures used.
3. Startup commands in separate subprocedure: Commands to place turtle in starting position in a separate subprocedure.
4. Navigating commands in separate module: Modular subprocedure used for commands to navigate turtle between squares.

Fig. 5.8 Year 1: Sally and George's Individual Solutions to the 'Four Squares' Task

(a) Sally's Procedures

```
TO SQU 4                TO START          TO FOURSOME
   START                   PU                 REPEAT 4 [FD 30 LT 90]
   REPEAT 4 [FOURSOME]     BK 100             LIFT
   END                     PD                 FD 50
                           END                PD
                                              END
```

(b) George's Procedures

```
TO SQ 4                          FD 50
   PU                            BK 50
   FD 130                        PU
   LT 90                         BK 20
   FD 20                         PD
   RT 180                        RT 90
   PD                            REPEAT 3 [FD 50 RT 90]
   REPEAT 3 [FD 50 RT 90]        FD 50
   FD 50                         BK 50
   BK 50                         PU
   PU                            BK 20
   BK 20                         PD
   PD                            RT 90
   RT 90                         REPEAT 3 [FD 50 RT 90]
   REPEAT 3 [FD 50 RT 90]        FD 50
                                 END
```

By the end of the third year of the project when Sally and George had experienced a more uniform set of tasks for which the ideas of structured programming were appropriate, they both produced similar programs, from the point of view of the use of subprocedure and modularity (Figs 5.9a and b). There was at this point no substantial difference between their solutions as indicated in their programs.

Fig. 5.9 Year 3: Sally and George's Individual Solutions to the 'Four Squares' Task

(a) Sally's Procedures

```
TO CUBE4              TO SKIP          TO CUBE
   SKIP                  PU               REPEAT 4 [FD 30 RT
   REPEAT 4 [CUBE]                        90]
                         BK 100           PU
   END                   PD               FD 40
                         END              PD
                                          END
```

81

(b) George's Procedures

```
TO SQ4
    MOVE2              TO MOVE2         TO BOX
    REPEAT 4 [BOX]     PU                  REPEAT 4 [FD 30 RT 90]
    END                BK 70               FD 30
                       PD                  PU
                       END                 FD 10
                                           PD
                                           END
```

As can be seen from Table 5.1, pupils when solving the 'Four Squares' task very rarely perceived a need to define separate 'navigating' modules. We have some evidence from other tasks (for example, the 'Decreasing Squares' task (Fig. 5.10)) that pupils are more likely to remove the navigating commands as separate modular subprocedures when a task involves 'picture' modules of varying size but invariant 'navigating' modules. This was also the case with the pupils' solution to the 'Row of Pines' task (Fig. 5.6).

Fig. 5.10 The 'Decreasing Squares' Task

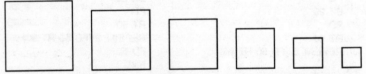

Linda, Jude, Shahidur and Ravi's uses of modular subprocedures in their solutions to the 'Four Squares' task were less sophisticated than the approaches of the other four longitudinal case study pupils. This is illustrated in the work of Shahidur and Ravi. Shahidur became a case study pupil at the end of the first year and Ravi at the end of the second year. Neither was given the 'Four Squares' task until the end of year two and they both tackled it in a similar way ... one long procedure with clear evidence of a global plan, but no use of subprocedures. At the end of the third year Shahidur again wrote one long procedure showing clearly that he had a global plan, but this time the computer ran out of memory and he could not include all the commands in one procedure. He asked for help and we said that he would somehow have to make the procedure shorter. Shahidur then, completely on his own, redefined his procedure to include a modular subprocedure to draw a square. It appears that his thinking was already structured so a nudge was enough to provoke him to break down his procedure into modules. He had during his class work used a modular approach when working on the 'Row of Pines' task (Fig. 5.6).

Ravi on the other hand (who was only a case study pupil for the last two terms of the Project) worked in direct mode on the commands to draw a startup, one square and interface. He then defined these as a procedure SQUARES and then added the command SQUARES at the end of the SQUARES procedure (this bug is discussed in Chapter 6). He was not able to debug this on his own and needed help in order finally to produce the row of four squares. We have observed pupils in the extended network also making this type of bug and we suggest that it arises from insufficient knowledge about Logo syntax and structure.

We can trace the reasons for these findings from the prior experience of these two pupils. We spent less teacher intervention time on the ideas of subprocedures with them, and they almost never initiated tasks for themselves in which the idea of sub-procedure could be introduced naturally.

We also gave the 'Four Squares' task to all the sixty-four pupils in our extended network of schools. At the end of the first year of the extended study, 4% of these pupils chose to use a modular subprocedure to solve this task and this only increased to 11% at the end of the second year. Analysis of the teaching and learning situation in the extended network schools indicates that the reason why the pupils had not used subprocedure as part of their solution was simply because they had not been introduced to these ideas during their 'hands-on' Logo sessions in school. Close examination of their solutions indicated that, as with the solution of George at the end of the first year of the project (Fig. 5.8b) many of the extended network pupils *had* a global plan of how to solve this task and this global plan showed a clear structure within their sequential list of commands. Our analysis of the extended network pupils' working procedures thus suggests that many of the pupils *could* have been introduced to the ideas of structured programming since they were already seeing the problem in a structured manner. It is possible from observation of pupils working at the computer and consideration of their written records to identify pupils who:

(a) have a clear, structured global idea of the task at the
    beginning of the session (for example, Fig. 5.8b);
(b) develop a structured approach to the solution as they work
    in direct drive (for example, Fig. 5.11);
(c) solve the task by trial and error without being aware of the
    overall structure of the problem (see, for example, Fig. 5.12).

83

Fig. 5.11 Structure Emerging

FD 45	FD 45	FD 45	FD 45
RT 90	RT 90	LT 90	LT 90
FD 45	FD 45	FD 45	FD 45
RT 90	RT 90	LT 90	LT 90
FD 45	FD 45	FD 45	FD 45
RT 90	RT 90	LT 90	LT 90
FD 45	FD 45	FD 45	FD 45
RT 90	RT 90	LT 90	LT 90
PU	PU	PU	
FD 65	FD 65	FD 65	
PD	PD	PD	

Fig. 5.12 No Evidence of Structure

		PU	PU	PU
		RT 90	RT 90	LT 140
		FD 20	FD 60	RT 90
		PD	FD 40	PU
FD 40	FD 40	BK 40	FD 140	
LT 90	RT 90	PD	PD	
FD 40	FD 40	FD 40	FD 40	
LT 90	RT 90	RT 90	LT 90	
FD 40	FD 40	FD 40	FD 40	
LT 90	RT 90	RT 90	LT 90	
FD 40	FD 40	FD 40	FD 40	
		RT 90	LT 90	
		FD 40		

We suggest that pupils in category (a) would be able to use the ideas of structured programming, pupils in category (b) may be able to use the ideas of structured programming and pupils in category (c) probably should not be introduced to the ideas of structured programming.

In conclusion, pupils' responses to the 'Four Squares' task from the point of view of using subprocedure and modularity was found, not surprisingly, to be related to their experience of using subprocedure during their 'hands-on' Logo time in school, and this in turn was closely related to the types of goals towards which they had worked. Their performance can be traced to the educational guidance received, either in the form of interventions during work on their chosen goals or in the form of 'teacher-devised' tasks. Thus we suggest that pupils are unlikely to adopt modular programming design unless we have developed an appropriate curriculum to introduce and reinforce its use.

PHASES IN WRITING PROCEDURES

We describe phases related to pupils' developing use of sub-procedure and modularity in their programming, the identification of which will assist teachers in discerning progression. The first phase relates to the development of an effective method of writing a procedure and later phases relate to how a procedure is seen as made up of subprocedures and/or modular subprocedures.

Procedures as Product

Phase 1a Writing an error-free procedure by direct driving and recording commands. No evidence of structure in the commands.

Phase 1b Writing an error-free procedure by direct driving and recording commands . . . structure emerging within the commands.

Phase 1c Writing an error-free procedure by direct driving and recording commands . . . clear evidence of structure within the commands, i.e. using modular ideas but not translating these into modular subprocedures.

Transitional Stage

Phase 2 Using the written record of direct drive work to perceive modularity in the design and defining these modules as subprocedures.

Procedures as Processes

Phase 3 Perceiving modularity from the outset and using sub-procedures to define the modules. (Pupils are more likely to define a subprocedure to draw a shape before they perceive a need to define subprocedures for the navigating between shapes (e.g. startup and interfacing).)

We suggest that whether or not pupils define subprocedures directly in the editor or try them out first in direct drive is a matter of preferred programming style rather than ability to use subprocedures in their program design. This was discussed in Chapter 4.

IMPLICATIONS FOR CLASSROOM PRACTICE

We suggest that pupils' use of subprocedures and modularity is influenced by both the nature and requirements of the pupil goals and the way these are perceived by the pupils. **It now appears that when pupils perceive their project to be one of working towards a real-world representation, the Logo commands are likely to become an extension of their drawing arm and subprocedures are defined only as a way of storing commands in a shorter sequential manner.** In such circumstances pupils do not perceive a need for their functional subprocedures to be reusable modules and consequently do not attempt to put interfacing commands into separate subprocedures. Pupils think out their commands in a step-by-step linear way and debug in a similar manner – that is, by correcting the image with commands at the end of their procedure and not debugging individual subprocedures. **When pupils work on more well-defined abstract goals they are more likely to plan their work in such a way that the idea of breaking a problem into parts and defining each part as a separate subprocedure is more easily introduced.** There is still a considerable variability between the pupils in their perception of modularity in a design. Pupils are more likely to use a modular programming style in tasks where the modules are 'disconnected' (for example, the 'Four Squares' task) than when the modules are connected. In addition pupils are more likely to choose modules which when put together do *not* involve drawing the same line more than once.

It now appears to us that we cannot discuss whether or not a pupil has used subprocedure and modularity without first addressing the issue of whether or not the pupil is working towards a well-defined or a loosely-defined goal. As stressed earlier, loosely-defined goals are important because pupils can learn about and explore the possibilities of subprocedure and modularity – the subprocedure is a tool for creative exploration. In contrast, in the context of a well-defined goal the subprocedure or modular subprocedure is an analytical tool which renders the structure of the problem more explicit. We cannot over-emphasise the importance of variety of experience – that is, work on both types of goal – but the teacher should recognise the different role subprocedure plays in the different contexts.

Studying pupils' final procedures from the point of view of subprocedure and modularity gives *no* indication as to whether or not the pupils solved the problem in a 'top-down' or 'bottom-up' way. Of the eight case study pupils only Sally and Asim appeared to adopt a predominantly 'top-down' style; that is, planning out the structure of a solution before starting to negotiate at the computer. We also suspect that the 'difficulty' (from the pupil perspective) of the goal will affect the style adopted by the pupil. We do think that it is important that pupils are allowed to adopt either a 'top-down' or a 'bottom-up' programming style. The Logo environment is in this respect important because either style can be used. In other programming languages it is often the case that the 'top-down' style is accorded more value. We now believe that the pupils' progress in being able to break down well-defined goals into subprocedures and modular subprocedures parts is a direct consequence of:

- Our nudges from the beginning stages of learning Logo to encourage the pupils to reflect on the process and state of the turtle within their procedures.
- Our interventions to suggest the idea of using procedures and subprocedure within projects for which these ideas were appropriate.
- Our interventions in the form of giving pupils well-defined abstract goals.
- The pupils' experience of building up subprocedures into loosely-defined goals and defining superprocedures for the final image.

However, our most significant finding is that pupils will *only* take on the idea of using subprocedure when this is a useful problem-solving tool. Often at the beginning stages of our project we suggested that pupils make their procedures more modular when it was not appropriate. One example of this was when George and Asim were working on a project to draw a rabbit's face (Fig. 5.4). We wanted them to remove the 'navigating' commands from their 'Bow-tie' subprocedure: 'You know we've got this thing about not putting the joining up in the procedure ... if you don't put it in, then you could use your bow-tie somewhere else couldn't you?' They did not take up this suggestion and why should they have done? Their rabbit's 'bow-tie' *belonged to this particular rabbit* and was not something which they would want to use again! Thus teachers need to be able to discriminate between projects for which the idea of subprocedure and modular subprocedure is useful and those for which it is not.

6

Some Common Pupil Misconceptions about Logo Programming

INTRODUCTION

From our work with the longitudinal case study pupils followed by observation of the extended network pupils, we have identified recurring misconceptions about the nature of programming in Logo. Most of these misconceptions are associated with an incomplete understanding of the sequential nature and the flow of control in Logo and arise if there is no teacher intervention at a crucial stage in the learning of Logo. Some of these conceptual bugs are particularly difficult for pupils to debug for themselves. We suggest they can lead to quite fundamental misconceptions amongst pupils about the nature of Logo if appropriate action is not taken.

This chapter will describe these frequently observed misconceptions and discuss the role of the teacher in helping the pupils to remediate them.

WHAT MODE AM I IN?

The majority of pupils taking part in the Logo Maths Project used RML (Research Machines Ltd) Logo. In this Logo the pupils can interact with the computer in two modes; the direct mode which produces a direct effect (either graphical, numerical or textual) and the editor mode. Procedures are defined and edited in the editor.

All of the pupils taking part in the project were introduced in direct mode to the turtle graphics subset of Logo. In this situation each command has an instant effect. As pupils started to define procedures we noted some confusions about whether they were in the editor or in direct mode. The RML version of Logo is helpful in this respect as the visual image on the screen, when in the editor, is very different from that obtained when in direct mode. Despite this, there was confusion. We have observed pupils using the BBC computer (with Logotron Logo) amongst the extended network pupils. In this system there is an additional 'defining' mode in which procedures can be defined before they are edited. This seems to increase pupils' confusion about 'where they are'.

We noticed that pupils who were confused in this way were likely to scrap procedures without debugging – that is, they tended to start from scratch every time their procedure had an error in it – and thus did not come to appreciate the power of the editor. We believe that pupils need a reasonable amount of time interacting with the computer in direct mode only – so they become comfortable with computer interaction and familiar with the idea of computer feedback. Then, when they are introduced to the editor, the teacher needs to point out explicitly the differences between the two modes and be alert for possible confusion.

FILENAMES AND PROCEDURE NAMES

We have observed, particularly in one of the extended network classrooms, that some pupils did not distinguish between the names of their procedures and the name of the file used to save the workspace on disk. Consequently, at the end of a session, pupils tried to save each procedure in a separate file with the same name as the procedure; for example, if they had defined a procedure called BOAT they used the command SAVE "BOAT thinking that this would save just the one procedure as opposed to the whole workspace. We believe that the confusion primarily stemmed from the teacher's own misconception when she first introduced the idea of saving and retrieving. In our view, to prevent this type of bug developing, it is important that filenames are chosen which are quite obviously distinct from procedure names; for example, we have used the initials of a pupil's name followed by the date... SAVE "AL1503.

LEARNING TO DEBUG

We have observed that in some classrooms the majority of pupils start again rather than attempt to debug a non-working procedure.

This may partly stem from the 'What-mode-am-I-in?' bug, but in our view it mainly arises from a lack of emphasis on reflection and an absence of teacher intervention at the crucial stage of learning how to define and debug procedures. Many pupils at the beginning stages of learning Logo choose for themselves projects which require a long list of sequential commands. When they try to debug this sort of procedure they often introduce more bugs during the debugging process. They therefore need teacher support to help them to be more systematic and to nudge them into completing the debugging process as opposed to starting a new project.

REPEATED STRUCTURES

Many of the extended network pupils were introduced to the REPEAT command in the context of building up rotated patterns. In this situation they tended to use the REPEAT command simply to generate an effect and did not reflect on the process and structure of the command. When they came to try to use repeated structures within well-defined goals, confusions became apparent related to the syntax, flow of control and operation of the REPEAT command. The following is an example of incomplete understanding of how repeated structures are programmed:

Fig. 6.1 The 'Four Squares' Task

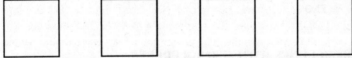

Whilst working on the 'Four Squares' task (Fig. 6.1) Linda first successfully used REPEAT to draw a square in direct mode:

```
REPEAT 4 [FD 30 LT 90]
```

Then still in direct mode she entered the 'navigating' commands to join this square to the next square:

```
PU
FD 40
PD
```

She then thought that she had solved the problem and confidently defined the following procedure:

```
TO SQUARE
    PU
    BK 100
    PD
    REPEAT 4 [FD 30 LT 90]
    REPEAT 4 [PU FD 40 PD]
END
```

We believe that Linda had a clear idea of how she wanted to solve the problem but that she did not know how to match the Logo syntax to her own problem solution. Linda, in this example, debugged her procedure herself by taking the construction of the drawing step by step as follows:

```
TO SQUARE
    PU
    BK 100
    PD
    REPEAT 4 [FD 30 LT 90]
    PU
    FD 40
    PD
    REPEAT 4 [FD 30 LT 90]
    PU
    FD 40
    PD
    REPEAT 4 [FD 30 LT 90]
    PU
    FD 40
    PD
    REPEAT 4 [FD 30 LT 90]
END
```

DIFFICULTIES WITH SUBPROCEDURES

(a) The Startup in the 'First' Module

Many pupils are reluctant to remove the interfacing commands from a 'picture' module even when there are strong visual cues to suggest that this should be done. This causes problems when pupils use such a module as part of a REPEAT structure. For example, Jude was working on the 'Four Squares' task. In direct drive he moved the turtle to the left-hand side of the screen and drew one square. He kept a record of these commands and defined a procedure BOX, which included start up commands and the commands for a square:

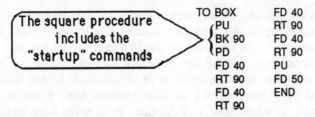

```
TO BOX        FD 40
 PU           RT 90
{BK 90        FD 40
 PD           RT 90
 FD 40        PU
 RT 90        FD 50
 FD 40        END
 RT 90
```

He had perceived modularity in the design and in order to draw the
row of four squares he defined the procedure:

```
TO BOX
  REPEAT 4 [BOX]
END
```

The computer feedback informed him that his solution was not
corr- ect. The teacher helped him to think through the sequential
process- es involved and he was then able to debug the procedure
himself.

(b) Unplanned Recursion

The unplanned recursion bug seems to occur when pupils perceive
a certain structure in a task but have insufficient experience of
using the ideas of subprocedure and superprocedure. They often
define a recursive procedure without being aware of the processes
involved. Ravi, before attempting the 'Four Squares' task, had
rarely used subprocedure either in building up a task or in breaking
down a task. All his previous projects had been focused on defining
and debugging a simple linear procedure. When presented with the
'Four Squares' task he tackled it in the following way.

In direct drive mode he drew a square and kept a written record
of his commands. He added the interface commands to join to the
next square and then defined the following procedure:

Fig. 6.2 Ravi's Solution to the 'Four Squares' Task

```
TO SQUARES
  RT 90       PD
  FD 40       SQUARES
  RT 90       PU
  FD 40       FD 5
  RT 90       PD
  FD 40       SQUARES
  RT 90       PU
  FD 40       FD 5
  PU          PD
  FD 5        SQUARES
              END
```

From this procedure it was very apparent that Ravi thought that the command SQUARES drew one square. This is how he had first conceived it – yet he added on the first interface so this was not how it had been defined! The procedure SQUARES drew Fig. 6.2. The recursive nature of the final procedure made it very hard to debug and he was not able to do this without help; it was in fact difficult to know how to help him. In a sense Ravi had too confidently defined the superprocedure in the editor when he was not familiar with the ideas. He needed a module for a square procedure and then this could have been used within a superprocedure. It seems that he had a good idea of the structure of the problem but again there was a mismatch between the structured solution, which he had devised, and his knowledge of Logo. We have frequently observed this bug amongst the extended network pupils. It poses a didactical problem for the teacher since it is difficult to know how to build constructively on the pupils' attempt without completely rewriting their procedures or telling them to start again.

(c) Flow of Control

The case study pupils were aware that they could increment a variable within a loop. They were introduced to this idea using a tail recursive structure. However, we found that some pupils overgeneralised the idea and tried to use it within other structures. This indicated an incomplete understanding of how control passed between Logo programs. We give as an example Sally's attempts at the 'Decreasing Squares' task (Fig. 6.3) at the end of the third year of the project. Sally defined a procedure to draw a variable square (with the interfacing commands included) as follows:

```
TO  BAG :SIDE
    REPEAT 4 [FD :SIDE LT 90]
    PU
    FD ADD :SIDE 10
    PD
    END
```

She then wrote the following procedure for the five decreasing squares:

```
TO  BIGBAG :SIDE
    REPEAT 5 [BAG SUB :SIDE 10]
    END
```

She then typed BIGBAG 60 and produced Fig. 6.4.

Fig. 6.3 The 'Decreasing Squares' Task

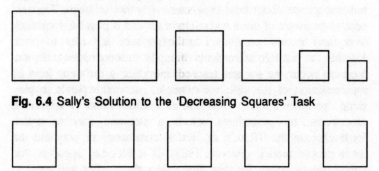

Fig. 6.4 Sally's Solution to the 'Decreasing Squares' Task

Sally was genuinely surprised at this outcome as she had obviously predicted that the sides of each square drawn would have been reduced sequentially by 10. Her work indicated some confusion as to how control is passed in Logo. She thought, however, that her confusion related to the REPEAT command and typed:

```
TO BIGBAG :SIDE
    BAG SUB :SIDE 10
    BAG SUB :SIDE 10
    BAG SUB :SIDE 10
    BAG SUB :SIDE 10
    BAG SUB :SIDE 10
    END
```

When trying this, the outcome was quite evidently no better than her previous attempt. She reflected as to why the image was the same. She eventually solved the immediate problem herself by 'going down a level' – that is, by using fixed subprocedures and thus avoiding the problems with flow of control. She wrote the following procedure:

```
TO BIGBAG :SIDE
    BAG 50
    BAG 40
    BAG 30
    BAG 20
    BAG 10
    END
```

This program allowed us to *see* what she wanted to do and help her in the construction of a program which achieved this outcome but in a more general way.

IMPLICATIONS FOR CLASSROOM PRACTICE

The bugs we have identified here indicate how pupils can build up misconceptions about how programming works in Logo. Teachers need to be aware of these potential pitfalls and if possible look back over their pupils' previous Logo experience in order to piece together the possible antecedents of pupils' misconceptions. If these bugs do occur we suggest teachers introduce a different form of representation of the task: for example, encourage pupils to play turtle, 'go down a level' – that is work in direct mode or with fixed procedures, try procedures out in a stepwise way to obtain feedback, use the TRACE or WALK commands or play out the 'little people model' (Harvey, 1985). If it becomes apparent that pupils cannot debug for themselves then the teacher will need to structure the learning situation in order to prevent the misconception from persisting.

7

Pupils Collaborating in a Programming Environment

At a theoretical level the educational world has long accepted the inadequacy of a model of teaching which is essentially one of transmitting a body of knowledge from teacher to pupil. In practice, however, the HMI publication 'Education Observed 2' (DES, 1984) reports that 'teachers need to have higher expectations of their pupils, to take greater account of pupils' individual differences and generally to make lessons less teacher-dominated'. This report also goes on to comment that most secondary school classrooms do not 'encourage pupils to develop arguments; to formulate, as well as to answer questions, and to articulate their ideas through more open discussion'. Mathematics educators since the publication of the Cockcroft Report are also more aware of the potential role of discussion in the mathematics classroom. As the Cockcroft Report stated, 'Language plays an essential part in the formation and expression of mathematical ideas. School children should be encouraged to discuss and explain the mathematics which they are doing' (Cockcroft, 1982, para. 306). Contexts are therefore being sought which provoke pupils to talk about mathematics and articulate their perspective on mathematical activities. Changing the emphasis in the mathematics classroom from a teacher-centred to a more pupil-centred approach to learning is not however an easy task as it involves a change in the teacher's role. Individualised learning schemes have started to shift the balance of control in classrooms but it is still the case that most pupils do not expect to discuss, collaborate and take responsibility for their own learning. The use of the microcomputer, in an interactive way, we hypothesised could provide the catalyst for further progress. The motivation of the graphical feedback and the public character of the screen would seem likely to stimulate investigative, pupil-centred work which could quite naturally be shared.

Mathematics educators have also turned their attention to the process by which discussion and peer collaboration can serve as aids to pupil learning. It is reasonable to conjecture that 'talking' (in both its cognitive and communicative functions) and listening (in an active way) generate increased understanding, facilitate integration of previously fragmented context-specific knowledge, and provide a bridge between the mathematics embedded in activities and its formalisation in standard mathematical notation. Research on peer collaboration effects has, however, been sparse. Such evidence that does exist which supports the notions of group work and discussion tends to be within a Piagetian framework and concerned with the notion of cognitive conflict. However, there is another way to achieve a shared task perspective and that is to assume complementary rather than conflicting roles. The work of Vygotsky offers insights into the intellectual value of inter-peer support, particularly with regard to 'scaffolding' the learning task (Wood, Bruner and Ross, 1976) in order that a partner might achieve a 'level of potential development' rather than a level of 'actual development' (Vygotsky, 1978). This idea has been taken up within a computer-based context in recent studies by Hoyles and Noss (1987, 1988).

In any exploration of these ideas it is important not to ignore the possibility that collaborative work, especially over an extended period of time, might impede individual acquisition of specific domains of knowledge and skills. Pupils tend to apply a 'division of labour' in group work and therefore may come always to rely on their peers for some aspects of the work (see Chapter 8).

While most educators agree that the microcomputer has the potential to promote interaction among pupils, there has again been little systematic investigation of the dynamics of the learning groups; that is, the individual responsibilities assumed, the kinds of interaction occurring and the effects of these interactions. Two of the aims of the Logo Maths Project were to investigate:

- the nature and extent of collaboration between pupil pairs learning Logo and differences in the collaborative patterns between pupil pairs;
- the influence of discussion between pupil pairs on the 'efficiency' of their problem-solving strategies and their understanding of programming and/or mathematical ideas.

SOME OVERALL COMMENTS AND ILLUSTRATIVE EXCERPTS

In the Logo Maths Project the pupils worked in pairs and were given the freedom initially to devise their own goals together. We found that this way of working within a supportive classroom climate provoked the pupils to come up with and struggle with challenging goals of a mathematical nature, and in so doing learn to articulate their thoughts and communicate and negotiate with their partners. We did, however, find that pupil pairs need time to learn to work together effectively. It is not sensible to expect pupils to discuss openly and share ideas if they have not had the opportunity to come to trust each other and to learn about each other's preferences and dislikes, strengths and weaknesses. We observed a qualitative development in collaborative skills over the three years of the project. Despite marked variation between the patterns of interaction between pupil pairs, instances for *each* pair were recorded when collaborative exchanges:

- provided challenging ideas for projects;
- kept the project going in the face of 'obstacles' and lapses in motivation;
- monitored the pair's activity – for example, recalled relevant past experiences;
- changed the focus of the work from local to global or vice versa in both planning and debugging stages;
- changed the form of representation of the activity – from a perceptual, action orientation to a more analytic, symbolic orientation or vice versa;
- provoked reflection on the process within a procedure to predict its outcome;
- encouraged/demanded systematic recording and checking and debugging.

We have looked at and compared collaboration within different types of programming activity for the same pair and have observed that within effective collaborative work the relative dominance between pairs varies according to the kinds of activity undertaken. We have also found that the longer the pupil pair work together, the more likely they are to adopt specific roles with respect to particular activities. This reflects an adjustment to the needs of the partner and the needs of the task. It does, however, have implications as to individual as opposed to group mastery over any particular understanding. Despite these reservations the following episodes serve to illustrate the three-way interactions between two pupils and computer feedback and the positive side to collaborative working.

JOHN AND PANOS

John and Panos were a first-year case study pair in the Project. Panos was an outgoing, friendly, talkative boy with a tendency to be impulsive and easily distracted. John, on the other hand, was quiet, reserved and thoughtful. John had an important role within the pair of 'managing' Panos, i.e. bringing him back to the work when his attention wandered and encouraging him to reflect and be more systematic. For his part, John obviously enjoyed working with Panos and benefited from his stream of exciting ideas. By the end of the first year both boys were able to demonstrate a remarkable ability to question each other and try to explain their ideas when their partner was confused. This is illustrated by the following excerpt in which the pair were defining procedures for regular polygons. They had already checked in direct drive procedures for a pentagon and a hexagon. Panos then confidently defined a procedure to draw a triangle in the editor:

```
TO TRI
    REPEAT 3 [LT 60 FD 20]
    END
```

John was not convinced that this would work: 'I'd laugh if it didn't work.' Panos then remarked: 'So would I ... well, I wouldn't actually laugh.'

Of course when they typed TRI the turtle did not draw a triangle! John was certain that he had known that it would not work: 'I knew it.' Panos was baffled and asked John to help out: 'Well, where did we go wrong?' John tried to explain but was really only at the stage of trying to sort out his own ideas: 'You went wrong with the ... what was it?'

John needed to look back at the procedure definition. He did this and tried again to explain in a rather halting fashion, making reference to the total turtle trip theorem: 'It can't be 60 you know ... that's 180 ... three 60's are 180 ... not 360.' Panos still did not understand John's reasoning but this discussion made him realise that he needed to return to direct interaction with the turtle rather than working in the editor – that is, change the form of representation of the activity. Panos said, 'We've got to do it slowly.' Panos started to draw a triangle in direct drive thinking aloud as he did it: '60 ... 60 ... it's 60, I'm sure ... 'cos remember equilateral triangles are 60 degrees ... and a triangle has 180 degrees angles ... so three 60's ... '

He did not recognise at this stage how the turtle drew an equilateral triangle and was simply recalling some facts he knew about equilateral triangles. John, however, wanted to try out his idea: 'Can I just try 120?' Panos was willing to let him try, although he was not convinced: 'Yeah ... I don't know if it will work ... ' John typed in:

```
REPEAT 3 [RT 120 FD 60]
```

and as the correct image emerged, John said: 'It does ... ' Panos was impressed but still wanted to know why: 'Voila ... how did you do that?' John could now confidently and clearly explain: 'It's 120 ... look it's 360 ... it's 360 around a point and you've got to ... so it's 120 ... ' The interaction assisted both boys; John became more articulate in his ideas and Panos began to identify the bug in his original argument 'that equilateral triangles always have 60''.

SALLY AND JANET

Sally and Janet were a longitudinal case study pair. As described in Chapter 3, Sally was an exceptionally shy pupil who lacked confidence in her own ability, but was considered by her mathematics teacher to be 'bright'. Janet was a bubbly, outgoing girl, about average in class for mathematics and loved using the computer. Janet and Sally were friends in and out of school. They both valued their collaborative Logo work. We found that Sally benefited from the collaboration because Janet provoked her into elaborating her ideas, thus helping her to think them through more clearly. Janet also provided a continuous source of suggestions, ideas and comments and thus kept the computer activity going – particularly as she became very proficient in Logo syntax. We think that Janet benefited from the collaboration because Sally was able to make decisions at a conceptual level about mathematical issues and explain her decisions to Janet. This helped Janet's understanding of the issues involved as well as complementing her perceptual approach with a more analytic perspective.

These findings are illustrated in the following extract. Sally and Janet wanted to make the turtle draw one and a half circles using the ARCR command. Janet wanted to enter:

    ARCR 40 360
    ARCR 40 180

However, Sally wanted to combine these commands into:

    ARCR 40 540

Janet did not understand what Sally was doing, so she questioned her: 'What you doing?' Sally started to explain: 'That will take it round to there.' Janet did not want to take the risk of trying something which she was not sure about. 'No, just do 180 . . . that will take it down to there.' Sally was insistent: 'Yes, I know, but . . .' Again, Janet disagreed: 'That's where we need it . . . ' This provoked Sally to elaborate her argument: 'Yeah. I know, but instead of doing two "commandments", you can just do one "commandment".' Janet asked her to elaborate more: 'How?' Sally replied without any general explanation – just giving the command required. This formalisation was important to clarify her thinking – for herself and for Janet. Sally said, 'ARCR 504.' Janet corrected Sally's arithmetic – indicating that she was at least following the argument: 'What, 504 or 540?' Sally then tried to explain again: 'Oh, 540 . . . that will take it round to there without having to do that . . . 'cos if you add that to that you get that . . . ' Janet, because she still did not understand, was prepared to question again: 'No, but . . . ' Sally now replied with a carefully reasoned explanation provoked by Janet's persistence: 'Say if you told me to walk 5 steps and I walked 5 steps . . . then you told me to walk another 5 steps . . . so I walked another 5 steps . . . you might as well tell me to walk another 10 steps . . . that's what I'm on about . . . ' The issue was resolved by Sally typing in ARCR 40 540.

Another episode from the data for Sally and Janet illustrates how the patterns of their collaboration changed during the different phases of the activity. This activity is based around the 'Spiral Task' and is described below.

Sally and Janet were given a sheet containing several spiral patterns (Fig. 7.1) and were told that they could choose to draw any of the spirals. We had found that pupils were more likely to engage in a problem and collaborate if given a choice from a set of tasks.

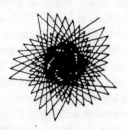

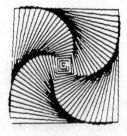

Sally and Janet decided to draw the square spiral. They perceived the task as one of drawing a square spiral shape which was similar to but not an exact representation of what was on the paper. One possible solution to the problem is:

```
TO SPIRAL :S
    FD :S
    RT 90
    SPIRAL ADD :S 10
    END
```

and we expected a similar solution. Our role was first to allow the pupils the freedom to develop their own solution to the problem and then to nudge the pupils into using a variable and operating on this variable within a procedure which matched the structure of the pupils' own solution. If the structure of the pupils' solution was recursive then we would introduce them to recursion in Logo.

103

Sally and Janet studied the square spiral and started to make a plan. Sally made a global analysis of the problem which she described to Janet: 'First we draw a line ... then we turn 90 ... add 10 and then we continue doing that ... turn 90 ... add 10 ... add whatever number we want.' Janet's next statement indicated a need to try out the plan at the 'hands-on' stage. She focused on the local details of the plan and how it could be executed in a step-by-step manner on the computer.

Janet said, 'Right, let's just see if it works ... so how long will the first line be ...? It can't be that long ...' Janet's disagreement provoked Sally into explaining that her example had been generic and not specific – she had introduced it to give an idea of the relationships in the task, not the details. 'No, not 10 ... I know ... I was just giving an example.' Janet was taking on the role of pushing Sally to attend to the local details of how to draw the spiral:

Janet 'So how big will the first line be ...? The actual line ...'
Sally 'Three.'
Janet 'Three?'
Sally 'Quite small.'

They typed in: FD 3 RT 90

Janet 'And what now?'
Sally 'It would have to be ... wait a minute! ... it's a square ...'

During Sally and Janet's collaborative work at the computer the 'hands-on' stage was very important in helping them to get started on a problem. After entering several commands they usually started another planning stage, with Janet at this point being more able to participate in the decision processes. They typed FD 4 and discussed the plan again.

Janet 'FD 4 ... no, hang on. This is what it would do. Look ...'
Sally 'You'd have to add two each time.'
Janet 'Look, say you do that, then that would be the same as that ... but this one would have to be longer.'

Sally was thinking that every FD command should increase in sequence, while Janet, now that she was involved, wanted to have *pairs* of equal FD commands! Sally conceded and worked it out on paper.

Sally 'Yeah.'

Janet 'So that would be the shortest one . . . so say that would be 3 . . . that would be 4 and that would be 4 . . . and that would have to be one smaller.'

Sally 'Work it out on here . . . look, that's the first one . . . make it go down like that . . . that must be one longer . . . and that has to be one longer . . . '

Janet 'And that has to be one longer . . . '

Sally 'No, those two can always be the same sizel . . . get me . . . ?'

Janet 'Yeah.'

Sally ''Cos look . . . '

Janet 'What you're really saying is those two are the same size . . . '

Sally 'Just add two . . . '

Whatever Sally's original plan she was willing to negotiate with Janet and between them they came to a shared understanding. Sally took the role of focusing the discussion on a global plan and Janet took on the role of attending to the immediate construction.

Janet 'So what you're really saying is those two are the same size . . . and those two are the same size . . . so how do we do that . . . ?'

Sally 'Alright. I'll make a quick REPEAT command.'

Janet realised that there was a problem with using the REPEAT command. They had only used the REPEAT command before to repeat a series of commands without incrementing a variable. 'Yeah, you'll have to . . . oh no, you can't REPEAT . . . no, you can't . . . 'cos you have to . . . '

Janet's language was not very explicit but the comment was important as it registered a worry about the potential problem with using the REPEAT command. For the time being they returned to trying out their plan in direct drive. Again they were using 'hands-on' activity to give them space to 'mull over' the problem.

After trying the sequence FD 3, RT 90, FD 4, RT 90, FD 4, they cleared the screen and started again with: FD 10, RT 90, FD 10, RT 90, FD 12, RT 90, FD 12, RT 90 (Fig. 7.2).

Fig. 7.2 Part of a Spiral

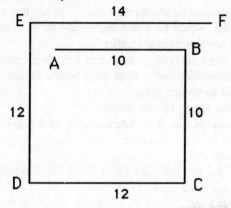

At this point Janet put forward an alternative plan and suggested that they make the next two commands FD 12, so there would be four consecutive FD 12 commands. Sally disagreed with this suggestion. Janet was still not clear and made her questioning more specific! 'No, hang on ... would it work if you said 10 10 12 12 12 12 14 14 14 14 ... ?' This question provoked Sally to elaborate her reply: 'No, 'cos these go up by 4 ... ' (meaning EF is 4 bigger than AB in Fig. 7.2) ''cos that is 2 and we want that to be 2 out as well ... so it's 14 ... '

Janet was not sure about this but the disagreement was resolved pragmatically by Sally typing FD 14 into the computer. They continued to type in the commands according to Sally's plan and as the image emerged Janet suddenly gained insight into the structure of the solution: 'I'm enjoying myself now ... it's all clear ... '

It is suggested that collaboration together with computer feedback enabled Janet to see the solution structure, so it was then just a small step to formalise a Logo program in a meaningful way. Eventually the pair defined the following procedure:

```
TO TEN :TWO
    FD :TWO
    RT 90
    FD :TWO
    RT 90
    TEN ADD :TWO 2
    END
```

Analysis of this one transcript in the context of all the longitudinal data highlights the following issues:

- Sally was able to see clearly a 'mathematical' relationship in the spiral. She could not at first easily express this in natural language until persistently provoked by Janet's questioning. This may be because she had difficulties with some of the local details of the generalisation. She also held back from expressing the mathematical generalisation in the formal language of Logo.
- Janet, on the other hand, was more concerned with actually drawing a specific spiral but needed help from Sally in order to come to an understanding of the general mathematical relationship in the spiral. She was, however, more confident about using the computer and about asking the teacher to help with syntax. In their working relationship she often took the initiative in this way.
- Both pupils have benefited from the collaboration. Sally provoked Janet to come to an understanding of a general relationship while Janet nudged Sally into using a variable to formalise the generalisation in the Logo program.

Other examples of collaborative work are given elsewhere in this book (see Chapter 3). It was evident that not only were pupils provoked to talk during their Logo work but also that a large proportion of the talk was task related – in contrast to findings of other research. For one pair, Linda and Jude, their talk began to deviate from the task during their second year of learning Logo. The type of social chat which these pupils engaged in was only remarkable because 'off-task' talk was so unusual. Although their social talk only took up a small part of their time on the computer we decided to change the pairing. They subsequently both worked with partners of the same sex. We continued to follow Linda and Elaine as a case study pair and with this pairing the amount of off-task talk decreased immediately and dramatically. The only occasions when the other pupil pairs engaged in off-task talk was when a procedure was slow to execute (often when the REPEAT command was being used) or when pupils were typing in commands which they had already planned out on a written record.

CODING OF PUPIL UTTERANCES

A classification system for the pupil discourse (Appendix 2) was developed in order to obtain an overall picture of the qualitative nature of the peer interactions, to facilitate comparisons between the pupil pairs and to monitor changes in interaction patterns over time. All the verbal 'on-task' utterances of each pupil during their Logo activity were coded using these categories. A pupil utterance was delimited by either an utterance of a partner or a specific action on the computer.

This analysis showed that most of the pupil talk was specifically action orientated; that is, focused on 'getting the task accomplished'. Little attempt, particularly at the initial stages of the Logo work, was made by the pupils to explain or convince one another of what was meant or why a proposed course of action should be taken. This was observed for all the case study pairs but particularly marked for boys. For further discussion of gender-related differences observed in the pupil talk, see Chapter 10.

A qualitative development over time in the language of the pairs was observable with a general move towards more elaborated argument and explanation. Despite this overall trend it is apparent from the tables of codings that other factors crucially influence the nature of interaction; in particular:

- the nature of the task (real-world representation or abstract);
- the extent to which the task is locally or globally planned;
- the extent of asymmetric negotiation and dominance of one partner;
- the extent of explicit (or even implicit) agreement as to overall strategy or plan;
- the extent to which pupils are 'getting on' socially.

INDIVIDUAL AND COLLABORATIVE WORK

As well as open-ended work, some specific structured tasks were set with particular aims in mind. Description and analysis was undertaken of collaborative interchanges which played an important role in the modification or reorientation of a pupil's conception of a mathematical or programming idea as identified previously in an individual setting. One example is given below:

Individual Work

Each pupil was given individually the 'Lollipop' task as shown in Fig. 7.3. This task was designed to investigate:

- whether the pupils individually were able to build a general procedure with variable input;
- how the pupil coped with the internal relationships assigned within the task;
- whether the pupil perceived modularity within the task; for example, whether a square procedure was used for the top of the lollipop.

Fig. 7.3 The 'Lollipop' Task

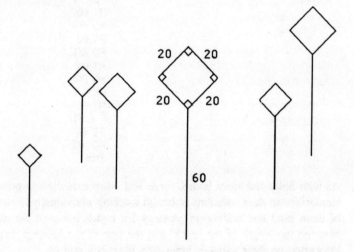

We were interested in whether the pupils would ignore the internal relationship given, employ an 'adding-on' strategy for inputs (that is, introduce a new input for each different part of the structure that 'varied' (see Hoyles 1987)) or make the relationship explicit by the use of a scalar operation on one input. **What is particularly interesting is that partners – now working individually – used very similar strategies.** Sally and Janet both wrote separate startup procedures, worked initially in direct mode recording their commands and introduced inputs at the point of building a procedure using a 'substitution' strategy – that is, replacing specific inputs to commands by named variables. Both girls used an 'adding-on' strategy for their variable inputs as can be seen from their final programs (Fig. 7.4). This indicated that they did not accord any importance to the relationship between the lengths 20 and 60 of the lollipop. In fact, both girls experimented with their procedures choosing inputs which did *not* represent this ratio in the figure. This is a nice example of the way pupils circumvent the situations we present to them – the girls just ignored the internal relationships assigned in the task!

Fig. 7.4(a)
Sally's 'Lollipop' Procedure

```
TO STICK :SIDE1 :SIDE2
    FD :SIDE1
    RT 45
    REPEAT 4 [FD :SIDE2 LT 90]
    END
```

Fig. 7.4(b)
Janet's 'Lollipop' Procedure

```
TO KITE :YT :HT
    RT 45
    FD :YT
    RT 90
    FD :YT
    RT 90
    FD :YT
    RT 90
    FD :YT
    RT 90
    FD :YT
    BK :YT
    RT 90
    FD :YT
    RT 45
    FD :HT
    END
```

As with Sally and Janet both George and Asim exhibited surprising similarities in their solutions although working individually. Neither of them used the 'adding-on' strategy for inputs but used the ratio between the length of the 'stick' and the side of the lollipop 'head' to operate on their variable input (see Figs 7.5a and b).

Fig. 7.5(a)
George's 'Lollipop' Procedure

```
TO SQUAN :NUM
    LT 45
    REPEAT 4 [FD :NUM RT 90]
    LT 135
    FD MUL :NUM 3
    END
```

Fig. 7.5(b)
Asim's 'Lollipop' Procedure

```
TO KITE :RAF
    LT 90
    FD :RAF
    LT 45
    REPEAT 4 [FD DIV :RAF 3
    RT 90]
    END
```

Both the boys' solutions implied a recognition of the relationship between the lengths at an explicit level. In fact, the solutions of

George and Asim are more similar than is immediately apparent from their final products because of their different starting points; George started on the 'head' and Asim started on the 'stick'. They both used the input variable to express the *first* unknown length in their procedure and then operated on this variable when they came to the second unknown length. George ended up, therefore, by expressing the relationship between the lengths as: stick length = 3 * side of head length; while Asim ended up by expressing it as: side of head length = stick length/3.

Collaborative Responses

Several weeks after the lollipop task the pupils worked in their normal pairs on the 'Arrow' task (Fig. 7.6). Let us take some selected interactions during Sally and Janet's work on the Arrow Task to see how they coped with the internal relationships within the task in comparison with their individual work on the lollipop. Overall, the coding of the pupils' utterances indicated a high overall level of elaborated argument. We shall, however, focus on the processes by which the pair working collaboratively negotiated how they saw the task, and developed a plan as to how it might be achieved.

Fig. 7.6 The 'Arrow' Task

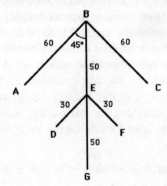

(Note: The lengths and letters were not included on the original task).

MAKE A PROCEDURE TO DRAW THIS SHAPE AS BIG OR AS SMALL AS YOU WISH.

The two girls first produced the figure in direct mode, their preferred working style. The figure they drew did not reflect the ratios given and AB was made to be equal to BE and twice as big as DE. At this point there was a detailed discussion of how the procedure should be built including elaborated arguments in the attempt to come to a consensus. The girls spontaneously saw that they could use the same input for AB and BE but wanted at the outset to use another input for DE as they had done in their individual work in the lollipop task – that is, use the 'adding-on' strategy. Janet explained her plan using language which did not refer to a general relationship but to a specific example: 'Alright ... we work it out 'cos that will have to be something called JACK and that JILL, if you get what I mean ... all the 50's, then the 25's.' They started to build a procedure:

```
TO HILL :JACK :JILL
   RT 90
   BK :JACK
```

At this point there was a 'critical incident' and Sally intervened: 'Wait a minute, you have to do ... no, BK MUL ... ' She wanted to operate on an input and tried to elaborate why in a general way: ' ... Em, you say for this one you say BK :JACK and for this one you multiply it by two 'cos that's half.'

Janet saw the structure but believed two numbers had to be used as inputs. Her argument was again very context specific. 'No, 'cos listen, look. But anyway, say that's 100 and we put in 100, then that would do that a 100, but you'd have to put in another number that ... So instead of putting in 2 numbers. Listen.' Sally seemed to become more confident in her idea in the face of Janet's conflicting perspective. She tried to justify her proposition and in so doing provided Janet with some 'scaffolding'. The pair discussed and they listened to each other. Sally took a global analytic view which incorporated the importance of preserving the relationship between the two lengths AB and DE while Janet focused on the local details of specific program construction:

Sally 'But we're not going to put any old number in 'cos it won't be the same pattern. Look ... '

Janet 'Yeah, but if you put in 75, then they're not going to be 75, they're going to be any old number.'

Sally 'Yeh, that's why we're going to multiply it.'

Janet 'Yeh, but you don't need to multiply it. That's what I'm
saying. If you say, em, if that one say that times by 2, it
would be that wouldn't it?'
Sally 'Divided by 2.'
Janet 'Yeh, you know what I mean.'
Sally 'Alright.'
Janet 'But I don't know how we're going to do it. We can get rid
of Jack.'

By the end of the interchange, Janet had agreed that they only
needed one input which could then be operated on to draw the
other length. In fact the pair retained the input of :JACK. When
they came to the line in the ARROW diagram which was the
smaller branch, they discussed what to do again:

Janet 'OK, so this go's FD dots divided by 2 . . . '
Sally 'JACK divided by 2.'

They both were a little muddled and still referred to the second
input they had previously used, JILL. None the less they managed
to resolve the difficulty together. It was interesting that they both
separately introduced JILL, yet both rejected their partner's
introduction of JILL! This seemed to have been significant for both
of them in coming to an understanding of how to operate on JACK.

Janet 'FD divide JACK divide by JILL.'
Sally 'No, no . . . Right so we want it to go forward by half of
JACK . . . so would that be JILL?'
Janet 'Yeh, I know, but just forget about JILL for the moment! How
do we do it?'

Sally then looked up the syntax (they did not ask the teacher) and
they decided to type in FD DIV :JACK 2.
 The final change in their procedure was to edit :JILL from the
title line of HILL. The pair then tried out their new procedure and
typed HILL 50. Their surprise and delight that it worked was
evident.

Janet 'Hey, it worked. I don't believe it.'
Sally 'Do it again. Do it again.'

They then tried HILL 70.

Sally 'Oh boy!'

Their final procedure for the ARROW is given in Fig. 7.7.

Fig. 7.7 Sally and Janet's 'Arrow' Procedure

```
TO HILL :JACK
    RT 90
    RT 45
    FD :JACK
    BK :JACK
    LT 90
    FD :JACK
    BK :JACK
    RT 45
    FD :JACK
    RT 45
    FD DIV :JACK 2
    BK DIV :JACK 2
    LT 90
    FD DIV :JACK 2
    BK DIV :JACK 2
    RT 45
    FD :JACK
END
```

It is evident from this analysis of the work on the ARROW task that the role of peer interaction in a computer environment involves issues which are extremely complex. However, there was evidence of a 'move' by the pupil pair here in the area predicted, that is operation of variables, as a result of the peer and computer interaction – there was *no* teacher intervention. The computer environment seemed to provide 'scaffolding' for the learning task and, in particular, observation of screen output was important. In addition, Sally was helped forward by articulating her thoughts and Janet by arguing with her and listening to the explanations.

IMPLICATIONS FOR CLASSROOM PRACTICE

It is by no means certain that pupils will make learning gains in tightly specified circumstances after collaborative work or discussion. It is difficult therefore for a teacher (or researcher) to predict with any precision what a pair jointly or individually will gain in any collaborative setting. We have examples of positive and negative collaborative effects which were completely unpredicted (and unpredictable!). Despite this we are certain that all the pupils have gained something from their partnerships in terms of presenting each other with challenges and encouraging persistence and variety in approach. We also found that the pupils learnt some independence of the teacher and the way the pairs of pupils learnt to collaborate together during their Logo work spread to their 'other' mathematical work and affected the level of discussion of mathematical issues within the mathematics classroom generally. We believe that this happened only because the computing work was seen as a natural part of the mathematics curriculum with the computer available in the mathematics lessons for use as and when appropriate.

8

Turtle Turn and Angle

INTRODUCTION

In this chapter we look at the other side of the coin with respect to group learning; that is, if we ignore social and motivational gains and simply concern ourselves with learning gains in specific areas, then it is possible to find a negative effect as a result of collaborative work. We shall illustrate this effect with reference to pupils' understanding of the notion of turtle turn in a Logo environment. The findings reported here have emerged from four sources:

* a detailed analysis and comparison of the transcripts of the work in relation to turtle turn of two longitudinal case study pairs of pupils (Sally/Janet and George/Asim) over the three years of the Logo Maths Project;
* the results of structured tasks on angle and turtle turn administered to all the case study pupils on an individual basis at the end of the project and a detailed analysis of the responses made by Janet;
* the results of similar structured tasks administered on an individual basis to the pupils in the extended network of the project;
* data obtained from structured interviews with the case study pupils.

It has been noted in previous research studies that the notion of angle is difficult for some children. For example, the results of the Assessment of Performance Unit (APU, 1985) in the United Kingdom indicate that many pupils think of angles in terms of length and area rather than in terms of turn. A common misconception in angle estimation is that pupils focus on such features as the lengths of the rays defining the angle, and the triangular area enclosed by these rays or the distance between their end points. This confusion between angular measure and measure of length or area has also been noted with respect to the sum of the internal angles of a triangle. Balacheff has reported that many pupils make the conjecture that 'the larger the triangle the bigger is the sum of the angles' (Balacheff, 1986, p. 5). It has also been found that pupils have a tendency to estimate the size of *any* acute angle as 45 degrees – even when contradictory information as to the size of the angle adjacent to it on a straight line or the reflex angle completing a turn is given (see, for example, APU, 1985).

It would seem reasonable to conjecture that the experience of working in turtle geometry would assist in the development of an understanding of angle. However, difficulties have been reported by researchers such as Papert et al. (1979), Hillel (1984) and Kieran (1985). Children do not necessarily perceive any relationship between turtle turn and angle. These limitations seem to stem from the way knowledge arises in a fragmented way and experience tends to be 'domain specific'. It has also been noted that some children use a restricted subset of inputs to RT and LT, such as repeated equal digits and multiples of 30 and 45 (see Chapter 11). The use of these subsets facilitates the production of a range of projects in turtle geometry but it is not clear that pupils are aware of the process by which their goals are constructed and the meaning of RT and LT; that is, the tools they choose to use define what can be done in ways that are not necessarily in the control of the user.

One important factor must be taken into account in a consideration of the findings reported below. The Logo Maths Project did not set out to investigate children's conceptions of turtle turn and angle. The researchers did *not* therefore make specific interventions to encourage the pupils to reflect upon the turns that the turtle had made or synthesise these with their notions of angle. The absence of such intervention is useful for research purposes in the analysis of the work of one pupil (Janet). We can deduce that it was the nature of the collaboration between Janet and Sally, the absence of appropriate teacher intervention together with the type of work they preferred to undertake which impeded the development of Janet's understanding of turtle orientation and turn, and consequently the synthesis of these notions with her conception of angle. In fact it was only when collaboration between the pair broke down because of an argument that Janet made progress of any note! In contrast, the nature of interaction between George and Asim in the context of the goals they chose did not provoke these problems.

THE WORK OF TWO PUPIL PAIRS

The analysis of Sally and Janet's programming work from the point of view of turtle turn brought the following to light:

- the pair only used turns of 45, 60 or 90 (except in the first few sessions when random inputs to RT and LT were used or inputs of 4 or 5 used to turn 'a little bit more or less'). In addition, Janet's *suggestions* for input were always restricted to this set of three numbers.

An obvious implication of this is that the pair never turned the turtle through an obtuse angle using one command only, although Sally suggested this several times. Obtuse angle turns (of 135 or 120) were sometimes 'needed'. In these circumstances the pair developed the following two strategies:

- for 135 they would turn 90 followed by 45 and later tidy this up to 135 when recording;
- for 120 (in the context of drawing an equilateral triangle) they would use inputs of 60 and combine these with moves backwards as well as forwards, i.e. FD 100 RT 60 BK 100 RT 60 FD 100.

In contrast the analysis of George and Asim's programming work from the point of view of turtle turn brought the following to light:

- the pair used the full range of inputs to RT and LT (including reflex and obtuse angles). It was apparent from their work that they had consciously made a synthesis between turtle turn on the screen and its effect on the angles of the figure obtained.

We are interested here in not only documenting the occurrence of these phenomena but also attempting to understand why they occurred. We should emphasise that we were not aware of these trends during the implementation stage of the Logo Maths Project – only after analysis of the transcripts collected over three years. Looking at completed projects or Logo programs or reflecting on individual sessions does not and cannot provide the more distanced and global perspective required. But first we shall attempt to capture the two pairs' work with respect to turtle turn.

Sally and Janet

As mentioned earlier Sally and Janet tended to embark upon loosely-defined abstract goals (see Chapter 4). They developed a consistent programming style in which a simple module was constructed and then built into a superprocedure during experimental 'hands-on' activity. This type of work provided important experiences in developing an understanding of subprocedure. However, little specific attention to turtle orientation or amount of turtle turn was required (except possibly in the definition of the original module as illustrated in the following episode). 'More-or-less' strategies worked and there was little need for an analytic approach with respect to local details.

After an exploration where the pair built a series of regular polygons, Janet was able to calculate the correct exterior angle for an n-sided polygon. She did this in paper and pencil mode by simply dividing 360 by the number of sides. She did not link the result of her calculation, however, to an amount of turtle turn and was not provoked to make this synthesis since she left these decisions to Sally.

For example, they were drawing a hexagon:

Janet 'Do it like 1, 2, 3, 4, 5, 6 sides. So what would 6 times 360 be . . . ? Have you got a pen, Sally? . . . Right, what's 360 times by 60?'
Sally 'Times by 6 . . . 60.'
Janet 'Of course, let's go.'

In this short collaborative sequence the pair had somehow communicated with each other that a '60' was the required 'number'. It is interesting to speculate, however, as to what the 60 *meant* for Janet as she went on immediately to suggest a turn of 45!

Janet 'How do I turn it up like that? . . . RT 45, I suppose.'
Sally 'Do it another RT 15.'
Janet 'No.'
Sally 'Each one of them is 60, remember, so do it RT 15.'
Janet 'Why RT 15?'

119

> Sally 'Each one of them . . . look. Right. Each one of them is 60
> and you've gone just RT 45 . . . well, that is 60 isn't it?'

Janet then followed Sally's instructions and typed RT 60 after each
FD command.

Janet's uncertainty about turtle orientation and turn was
particularly apparent (in retrospect!) when the pair were trying to
tessellate hexagons. The girls had 'fallen out' so Sally was refusing
to take her normal role of suggesting the turns required!

> Janet 'I need to go that way.'
> Sally 'Well, go ahead then.'
> Janet 'How though?'
> Sally 'Just twist it.'

For the first time in their year and a half together Janet was forced
to make a final decision. Fortunately a turn of 60 was required –
one of her known set of inputs to RT and LT! After some thought
Janet typed LT 60 and was both surprised and pleased that she was
right! However, it was not long before she gave up on the project
as she found the turtle navigation too hard to do on her own.

**In analysing Janet's contribution to future projects we see
that she continued to fail to make any synthesis between her
'arithmetic', 'turtle' and 'angle' frames – between her actions at
the computer, the symbolism in her programs and the visual
outcomes.** She used and tidied up inputs to RT and LT but did not
reflect on the implications of the result in terms of total turn nor
relate the result to the angles in a given figure. She performed the
arithmetical operations appropriate for the calculation of turtle turn
but then only suggested turtle turns of 45, 60 or 90 which were then
subsequently amended by Sally. Over and over again we can now
see that Janet could express what she wanted to do in general or
global terms but could not work out the local details, as illustrated
in the following extract:

> Janet 'We have to make the angles so it will go like that and
> like that. How do we do that?'
> Sally 'LT 30.'

Alternatively, Janet opted for her 'standard' set of inputs without analysis of the geometry of the figure or use of any angle estimation skills:

Janet 'Shall I do 45?'
Sally 'No, it will be something like 50.'
Janet 'No, let's just use 60 – it will probably go down that line anyway, won't it?'

Janet's responses here should be seen in the context of the particular goals of the pair's activity. When working on well-defined projects, only turns of 45, 60 and 90 were used; when working on loosely-defined projects the turns required emerged during the action of constructing the pictures on the computer in a perceptual way. Thus the final turns sometimes included a wider range of numbers than 45, 60 or 90 but these turns were not constructed analytically. The pupils did not therefore reflect on the relationship between the turns made and the angles within their picture, nor did they reflect upon any angular relationships implicitly used in the picture's construction.

George and Asim

Sally and Janet's projects contrast with the well-defined, real-world goals preferred at an early stage by another case study pair, George and Asim. These boys always planned out their work very carefully on paper. They regarded 'hands-on' activity as a way of simply testing out and debugging a sequence of preplanned commands. This style of working involved a focus on turtle orientation and turn at the planning stage. This background had very obvious influences on their approach to subsequent work at the computer, as we shall describe in the following example.

During their sixth session of learning Logo, George brought to the lesson several procedures already planned. He had worked out a procedure to draw a face using a self-devised grid to help with the turtle steps (Fig. 8.1). Thus he had consciously linked up his figure with turtle moves.

Fig. 8.1 George and Asim: The Face

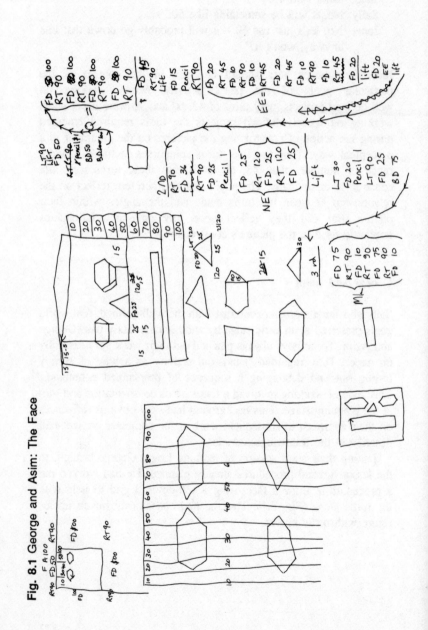

The pair did not in fact use one of George's planned projects but chose to draw the turtle on the front of the handbook (Fig. 8.2).

Fig. 8.2 Planning for a Turtle

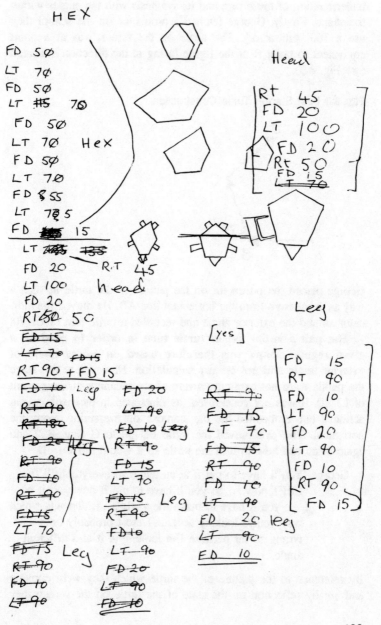

They did not discuss an overall plan. First they measured the lengths on the 'handbook' turtle and decided to double all the distances. They then considered how to turn the turtle. This appeared to be a critical incident in the development of their understanding of turtle turn and its synthesis with the angles within the shape. Firstly, George fetched a protractor (in the school they use a 360° protractor). The turtle on the screen was at a point equivalent to point B of the figure facing in the direction indicated (see Fig. 8.3).

Fig. 8.3 First Step in Turtle Construction

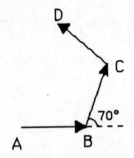

George placed the protractor on the picture of the turtle in such a way as to measure from the horizontal line AB. He moved the indicator around the exterior angle and recorded a turtle turn of LT 70.

The pair's initial use of turtle turn in order to produce a given regular shape was therefore based on *measurement* of exterior angle and not on any calculation. However, at this stage the pupils were not explicitly aware of the meaning of their result of LT 70. It was not generalised (as illustrated in their subsequent actions) but embedded in the context of measuring from the horizontal. The pair moved the turtle FD 50 to C (Fig. 8.3) and again discussed how to turn the turtle so it would move to D.

> George 'You'll have to put it at an angle so everything'll fit
> LEFT now . . . so you'll have to put it down a bit now
> . . . you'll have to make the angle . . . it depends which
> way you're looking at it . . . I most probably been
> wrong so far because I'm looking at it at a different
> angle.'

By reference to the picture of the turtle which they were copying and *not* by reflection on the state of the turtle on the screen they

decided to turn LT 115 at C; that is, they input a turtle turn equal
to the estimated size of the *interior* angle of the pentagon on their
paper. **At this point they were not able to hold in their minds
simultaneously the turtle state and the angle of the shape.** The
fact that the base line from which the turtle turn was to be
measured was no longer horizontal was sufficient to 'upset' the
tentative links that had been in their initial moves. The screen
output indicated to them, however, that they had made an error:

Asim   'It's too much.' (meaning the turn)
George 'OK, let's put it back.'

Asim then realised that since their left turn of 115 was too much,
they could compensate for this by turning right by an amount
smaller than 115.

Asim   'What do you mean, put it back RT 115 . . . it's not worth
       it.'
George 'Yes it is.'
Asim   'Just take a bit of it off.'
George 'OK.'
Asim   'You don't have to take it all off.'

Then followed what appeared to be a critical interchange. Both
pupils had been focusing on turtle state on the screen. They were
trying to 'see' how far to turn the turtle back using estimation.
George suddenly brought 70 into the discussion – that is, the
amount turned previously at B.

George 'Minus 70.'
Asim   'Minus 70. . . RT 70.'
George 'No, minus 70, um . . . OK . . . no, 115 minus 70.'
Asim   '115 minus 70.'
George '45 . . . RT 45 . . . RT 45.'
Asim   'That's wrong.'
George 'It's not . . . 45.'
Asim   'I know that.'
George 'RT 45 FORWARD 50.'

George's introduction of 70 seemed to trigger a link with their
earlier measurement and in the short interchange the pair moved
from perceptual to analytic mode. Implicit in their decision to turn
RT 45 was the beginning of a strategy that the turn at every vertex
of the figure should be LT 70. This is indicated by their subsequent
actions when the turtle was at D. George suggested a turn of LT 70

125

after which the pair completed the figure quickly, with an immediate decision to turn LT 70 at every vertex.

George	'LEFT 90 . . . no, 70.'
Asim	'70 . . . LT 70.'
George	'FORWARD 7 . . . FORWARD 50.'
Asim	'LEFT 70.'
George	'LT . . . where's the L . . . are you writing this down?'
Asim	'Oh yeh . . . wait a sec . . . wait a sec . . . LEFT 70.'
George	'I'll try it quick so I can get used to it.' (meaning typing)
Asim	'There . . . perfect . . . 50 . . .'
George	'FORWARD 50 . . . hopefully.'

At this point the pair knew that the turtle 'drew' by reference to exterior angles. This 'fragment of knowledge' was not, however, synthesised with any notion of a total turtle turn of 360. Their focus on turtle state and their continued endeavours to synthesise turtle turns and the angles required to produce a given figure is illustrated by the next stage of the above project.

The pair had made the turtle's body ABCDE (Fig. 8.4) and moved the turtle to point X. They wanted to draw a triangular head XYZ. This required a careful and explicit awareness of the relationship between the angles of the figure and turtle turn.

Fig. 8.4 The Turtle

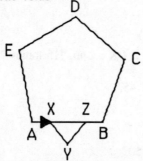

At first they were confused between turns of left and right and which angle in their picture related to turtle turn. **At several points in the subsequent discussion and during attempts to explain to each other what was happening they *explicitly* focused on which way the turtle was facing and how much the turtle needed to turn.**

Asim   '45, no, hold it. That's going straight, that would be 90 . . . no, 180, this way . . . 135 . . . LT 135.'

They reflected on what happened.

Asim   'What's 225?' (they had turned LT 135 and then LT 90)

George   'From there . . . the angle . . . the angle of turn.'

They then debugged using a combination of analytic and perceptual cues.

Asim   'If that's what you are going to do, that's wrong.'

George   'Yeah, I know . . . that's straight (indicating which way the turtle is pointing) so we have to turn it . . . 90 . . . what's 90 plus 45 . . . 13 . . . LEFT 135.'

Asim   'That's wrong again . . . look at the TV a minute . . . I think it should be a little bit this way.'

The significance of this activity was in its continuous 'to and fro' between turtle state on the screen, turtle turn and how the shape was actually being built up.

The way the pair continued to use the image of measuring with a 360° protractor to help them 'see' the turtle turns is illustrated in a later episode. During their eighteenth session of learning Logo, George and Asim were working on a project to draw a ball moving across the screen into a goal post. Although they normally preplanned their projects on graph paper they worked on this project in 'hands-on' mode at the computer discussing amount of turn and distance at every point. Drawing the goal post itself involved considerable negotiation of turtle turn as the following extracts illustrate:

Fig. 8.5 The Goal Post

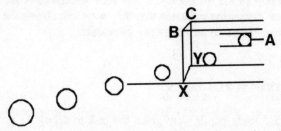

George and Asim were aiming to draw Fig. 8.5. The turtle was at B pointing in the direction AB. George confidently told Asim that the next turn should be RT 135 and they entered this command. As the turtle turned, Asim indicated that he was watching the effect of the computer input by his comment, 'Yeah, perfect ... this is fun this.' They then discussed how much to make the distance command and entered FD 15 followed by FD 5. Now with the turtle at C pointing in the direction BC they wanted to draw the line CY. They both appeared to have a strategy for calculating the exterior angle which directly linked to an idea of measurement with a full circle protractor. They seemed to imagine (initially) a protractor placed on the line BC centred at C (see Fig. 8.5) with the pointer towards B. The turn of this pointer so it ended along CY would be a reflex angle which they estimated (wrongly!) as 250.

Asim	'How much?'
George	'Wait a sec, if it's facing there we want to go from 180 to 250.'
Asim	'130.'
George	'No.'
Asim	'Yes.'
George	'It's not.'
Asim	'To 250, isn't it ... '
George	'No, from 180 to 250.'
Asim	'Oh.'
George	'70.'
Asim	'70.'

They entered RT70, and then debugged this until the turtle had turned through 135. They then negotiated the next distance command and entered FD 25 followed by FD 5. The turtle was now at Y pointing in the direction CY and they wanted to move to X. Again their discussion indicated that they were calculating the turtle turn with reference to an imaginary protractor.

SOME STRUCTURED TASKS

All the case study pupils were given the task to debug the program for an M as shown in Fig. 8.6.

Fig. 8.6 The 'M' Debugging Task

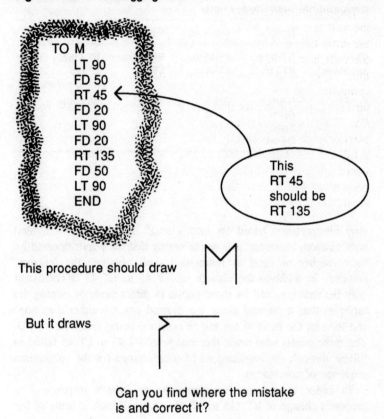

```
TO M
    LT 90
    FD 50
    RT 45  ←
    FD 20
    LT 90
    FD 20
    RT 135
    FD 50
    LT 90
    END
```

This
RT 45
should be
RT 135

This procedure should draw

But it draws

Can you find where the mistake
is and correct it?

An analysis of the results is presented in the following table:

Table 8.1 Analysis of Results of the 'M' Debugging Task for Longitudinal Case Study Pupils

	Correct	Incorrect	Incorrect	Incorrect
Change suggested	RT 45 to RT 135	RT 45 to LT 45	RT 135 to LT 45	RT 135 to LT 135 (no other change)
Pupils	George Asim Sally Elaine	Jude Linda Ravi	Janet	Shahidur

Any interpretation based on such a small sample must be treated with caution. However, it is worth noting that the pupils deemed by their teacher as good at mathematics all obtained the 'correct' solution. In addition the change of RT 45 to LT 45 is consistent with the strategy used by those pupils in direct mode of turning the turtle so that it pointed along the desired line (in either direction) and then on the basis of the screen outcome using either BK or FD. The three pupils who made the change of RT 45 to LT 45 failed to follow through the implications of their change for the subsequent sequence of commands.

In order to aid our interpretation of Janet's response – a proposed change of RT 135 to LT 45 – we will look at some of her work on other structured tasks.

Janet's Responses

Janet's debugging of the 'M' task consisted firstly of changing the initial LT 90 to RT 90 (the initial state of the turtle points to the right), and secondly to change the RT 135 to LT 45. Her program for M is as shown in Fig. 8.7.

Janet's first error, that is changing LT 90 to RT 90 for the first command, is indicative of her problems of lateralisation. Janet, throughout her Logo work, found it difficult to work out whether to turn left or right. Janet's score on an Embedded Figures Test (Witkin et al., 1971) indicated field dependence. She tended to rely

Fig. 8.7 Janet's Procedure for 'M' Debugging Task

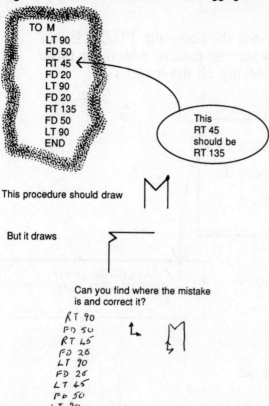

```
TO M
    LT 90
    FD 50
    RT 45  ←
    FD 20
    LT 90
    FD 20
    RT 135
    FD 50
    LT 90
    END
```

This
RT 45
should be
RT 135

This procedure should draw M

But it draws

Can you find where the mistake
is and correct it?

```
RT 90
FD 50
RT 45
FD 20
LT 90
FD 20
LT 45
FD 50
LT 90
```

on the screen output after the turn to make a decision as to whether
to go forwards or backwards. Her second error, that is the change
of RT 135 to LT 45, can be interpreted as an unfamiliarity with and
therefore avoidance of obtuse angles in a turtle context together
with a focus on the internal angle of the M rather than on the path
of the turtle.

131

Fig. 8.8 Janet's Attempt at the 'Puzzle' Tracing Task

If I type into the computer PUZZLE can you draw out the pattern which the turtle makes marking all the lengths?

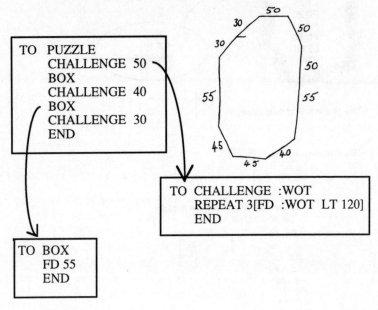

```
TO   PUZZLE
     CHALLENGE 50
     BOX
     CHALLENGE 40
     BOX
     CHALLENGE 30
     END
```

```
TO  CHALLENGE :WOT
    REPEAT 3[FD :WOT  LT 120]
    END
```

```
TO  BOX
    FD 55
    END
```

This interpretation is supported by Janet's response to the PUZZLE task as set out in Fig. 8.8. Janet's sketches exhibited a good understanding of the sequential process within the PUZZLE procedure; that is, she knew she had three lots of lengths of 50 followed by an FD 55, then three further lengths of 40, etc. She then used what we term an 'interior angle strategy' – that is, she places herself at the vertex of the angle facing down the ray she has just drawn and then turns LT 120. This is of course equivalent to a turtle turn of RT 60. We hypothesise that she would only use this strategy when faced with an input to RT or LT of over 90.

Fig. 8.9 Janet's Attempt at the 'Pat' Tracing Task

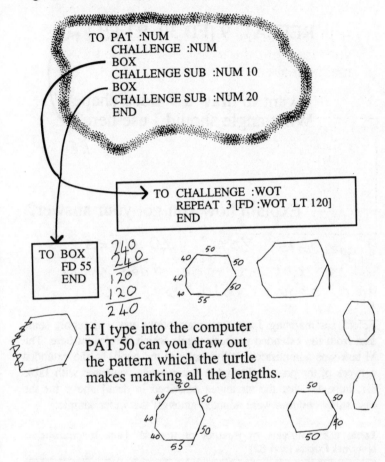

If I type into the computer PAT 50 can you draw out the pattern which the turtle makes marking all the lengths.

When Janet came to attempt the PAT task she adopted a very similar strategy as shown in Fig. 8.9. She appeared to understand the control process in the Logo procedure and how the values of the variable :NUM changed for the different calls of the subprocedure CHALLENGE. Her only misconception related to the turn of LT 120 within CHALLENGE. The fact that she was quite able to calculate in a formal sense the angles required for a total turtle turn is illustrated in her response to the REPEAT task as shown in Fig. 8.10. Janet knew on this level that the input to RT for a 9-sided shape should be 40 but she was not relating this to the turtle turn in her work on the computer.

Fig. 8.10 Janet's Attempt at the 'REPEAT' Task

REPEAT 9 [FD 30 RT 40 [?]]

I want to draw a 9 sided shape
What angle should I use here?

40

Explain how you got your answer?

9 goes into 360° 40 times
So to get a nine sided shape
your angle would be 40

Before summarising Janet's misconceptions we will report some data from the extended network pupils which is relevant here. The M task was administered individually to the pupils in the extended network of the project. The table below, when compared with Table 8.1, indicates that the strategies described in detail above for the case study children were adopted amongst the wider sample.

Table 8.2: Analysis of Results of the 'M' Task for Extended Network Pupils (n = 62)

	Correct		Incorrect		Incorrect		Incorrect		Incorrect	
Change suggested	RT 45 to RT 135		RT 45 to LT 45		RT 135 to LT 45		Other changes to RT 135		Other	
	N	%	N	%	N	%	N	%	N	%
No. of pupils	15	24	15	24	14	23	9	15	9	15

These results provide a framework from which to view Janet's responses. We suggest that taken together we must be aware that when working in turtle graphics:

- pupils may have problems distinguishing RT and LT;
- pupils may not engage in experiences which provoke them to reflect upon turtle turn;
- pupils may not synthesise turtle turns with angles in a shape and with calculated values. Put another way, pupils may have separate frames for calculations of inputs to RT and LT, geometric relationships and perceptual interactions at the computer.

INTERVIEWS WITH THE CASE STUDY PUPILS

At the end of the Logo Maths Project all the case study pupils were asked to write down a procedure which would draw a square. This they all managed to do very easily. They were then asked firstly why they had used 90 as an input to the turn command and secondly if they drew a square on a piece of paper could they indicate on the figure what the meaning of the turn of 90 was. Six of the case study pupils labelled the interior angle of the square as 90, saying this is what they meant by the turn of 90, as shown in Fig. 8.11a. One of the case study pupils made an ambiguous labelling Fig. 8.11b.

Fig. 8.11 Pupils' Interpretations of 'Input of 90'

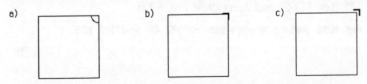

Janet made an interesting response: when asked to point to the 90 she indicated a turn round the vertex and said: 'That one, and if you're going along like that it would be that one.' When asked to draw it on a diagram of a square she produced Fig. 8.11c.

The pupils were also asked to write a procedure for a regular 6-sided shape. This again caused no problem but when asked to draw the hexagon and point to the turn of 60 which they had put in their procedure, the same six pupils (including all the four deemed good at mathematics) once again labelled the interior angle. Janet's response is again worth recording in more detail. First when asked why she used 60 she replied immediately in her calculation frame: 'Ah . . . to do 6 goes, that's how many times you're going to do 60.'

When asked to draw it she produced Fig. 8.12, labelling a type of exterior angle. **Janet appeared to know that the turtle somehow turned all the way around the 'outside angle' but this knowledge did not conflict with her answer of 60. For her at this moment her calculated '60' had nothing to do with angles of 60 degrees.**

Fig. 8.12 Janet's Response to Request to Label 'Turn of 60' in a Hexagon

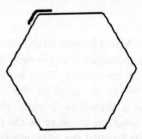

In order to explore still further Janet's conception of angle and turtle turn the researcher asked her to trace out what would happen if the turtle moved FD 50 then RT 45 and then another FD 50. Janet produced the following (Fig. 8.13a). The researcher then asked her to trace out what would happen if the turtle moved FD 50 then RT 135 then FD 50 and Janet drew Fig. 8.13b.

Fig. 8.13 Janet's Interpretation of 'RT 45' and 'RT 135'

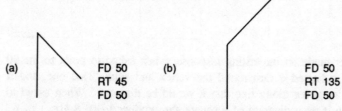

(a) FD 50   (b) FD 50
     RT 45   RT 135
     FD 50   FD 50

The researcher then intervened to suggest that she had made a mistake and Janet made the following interesting response: 'No, I was thinking that . . . that that would be the 45, the angle . . . that way I wasn't really thinking of the turtle turn, I was thinking that's the angle.'

Janet's behaviour and indeed her final comment indicated clearly how she changed her interpretation of inputs to turtle turn according to context. She did however consistently adopt what we have termed earlier in this chapter an 'interior angle' strategy which converts turtle turns to interior angles.

IMPLICATIONS FOR CLASSROOM PRACTICE

It has been a salutary but informative experience to look at all the three years of Janet's Logo work with a focus on her understanding of turtle turn. Before this analysis we had no indication of the fragmented nature of her conceptions. Many screen images were 'rotating' in ways that the pair had planned – either because simple arithmetic had been used to calculate the 'number' to use as input to the turn command or Sally had made the 'right' decision. In addition, the pair's final programs often incorporated what seemed to be 'obtuse angles'. Janet's continued uncertainty with amount of turn and turtle orientation was completely hidden from the researchers at the time. Her lack of analysis over these local concerns contrasts with her skills in modular program design and use of variable input to general procedures. Our interventions focused on these latter two ideas so we can only deduce that these interventions were crucial. It is possible that the way the turtle turns in the version of Logo used by Janet contributed to her misconceptions and her development of the interior angle strategy. It is also possible that turtle graphics may actually inhibit reflection in any analytical way since it is difficult to 'see' what is happening or detect visually whether a correct sequence of commands has been used. Undoubtedly the asymmetric dominance between Sally and Janet over this particular knowledge domain further complicated the matter, especially in the context of the type of goals they chose which did not demand a predetermined negotiated plan.

It should be noted that Sally achieved correct results for all the individual tasks described in the previous section. We looked back at our research data to see if we could identify a time or times when Sally specifically made the connection between input to RT and LT and angle. We found (to our surprise, as we had forgotten!) that on her second session Sally was paired with George and they decided to reproduce a simple shape without going over any line more than once. It was during this project that the pair decided on inputs to RT and LT of 120 without having to iterate. From that point onwards they both, individually, were able to analyse a figure and calculate the angles required for turtle turns. How George came to do this with Asim is illustrated in this chapter. Again the type of goal – with a well-defined plan of local details – was important. Also the way the pair collaborated is of significance. The girls seemed to have an implicitly agreed 'division of labour' in their Logo work with Janet controlling the experimental activity and the keyboard while Sally made decisions about the turtle turns. The boys in contrast did *not* 'agree' to allow dominance by one partner of one aspect of the computer activity.

The case study of Janet suggests that pupils may not perceive inputs to RT and LT as rotations in circumstances where the nature of these inputs is determined by the context; that is, there is use of rotation without reflection on what turn has been made or synthesis with angle in other contexts. In such situations children compute inputs to RT and LT, add and subtract them or compose them at the level of action but do not necessarily synthesise their resulting input to a total amount of turn; put another way pupils might be adding and subtracting numbers or adding and subtracting actions but not angles! It should be noted here that when pupils only use multiples of 45 in their turtle graphics work the whole issue of the link between turtle turn and the exterior angle of any shape is actually never confronted. The data from the extended network also suggests that pupils may continue to be confused about turtle turn without more specific teacher intervention.

It is important to note here that the pupils' perception of what they are learning is not necessarily in this case helpful. When Janet in her final interview was asked whether she thought her Logo work had in any way helped her mathematics she immediately replied: 'Ah, yeah, with sort of like the angles . . . you sort of have to work the angles out.' This comment certainly described Janet's behaviour. Yes, certainly she 'worked the angles out' in a formal sense but what she never did was link this with turtle turn or make the decisions about estimated angle turn when working in direct mode.

Finally, we would regard reflecting on turtle turn and its synthesis with angle conception as a 'local' issue in the construction of a turtle graphic goal. Janet, as we have suggested, reflected on global structures but not on these local details. In contrast, George (particularly at the earlier stages of his Logo work) worked hard on local details. He and Asim liked precision and this provoked them to measure angles with a protractor – which we suggest was crucial to their eventual synthesis of angle in shapes and turtle turn. At the time we did not recognise this but noticed only George's lack of experimental work and reflection upon global structure. We actively encouraged the boys to move from a local to a more global view, since we recognised the need for a combination of holistic style with attention to detail. The following question is now food for thought for us as it perhaps reflects our own biases! Why did we not think to encourage Janet to move from her global planning to more attention to local detail? This suggests that teachers should not only be aware of pupil dominance in a pair but also be aware of their own biases!

9

The Teacher's Role

INTRODUCTION

At various times in the recent history of mathematics education
there have been initiatives to develop teaching styles and promote
variety in teacher/pupil interactions in the mathematics classroom.
It is probably fair to say that most of these initiatives have not been
successful on any wide scale. In the Modern Mathematics
movement in the 1960s, for example, there were twin intentions –
new content and new ways of learning. The former intention was
fulfilled; sets and matrices for example appeared on syllabuses but
there was little evidence of the latter – which obviously had a
negative influence on the success of the movement overall. Later
the Cockcroft Report (Cockcroft, 1982) explicitly proposed that
there should be more discussion in mathematics classrooms together
with more practical and investigational work. Such proposals imply
a role for the teacher as a guide and facilitator within pupils'
mathematical activity rather than a transmitter of a body of
knowledge into a set of 'empty vessels'. Despite such proposals
emanating largely 'from above', variety in mathematics teachers'
strategies could still be said to be limited – perhaps because of the
constraints built into the classroom situation and the reciprocal and
self-reinforcing expectations teachers and pupils have of each
others' roles.

The introduction of computers into mathematics classrooms is
quite widely seen as a catalyst for change in pupil-teacher relations
with pupils more likely to make decisions and, to some extent, set
their own learning agendas. As Weir (1987) claimed (in the context
of Logo programming) 'the most exciting part of the educational
computing enterprise will be its effect on classroom culture: the

attitudes and atmosphere and the patterns of intervention, and *on the location of control in the classroom*' (p. 246) (our emphasis). Computers are not, however, a panacea. It is all too easy to merely fit their use into existing practice or 'hive them off' into a separate compartment leaving the curriculum essentially unchanged. In the Logo Maths Project we sought to clarify and evaluate a framework of teacher strategies which integrated the Logo work with the mathematics curriculum in ways within which we hope teachers would find it possible to work.

WAYS OF INTERVENING

Our study has highlighted the crucial influence of the teacher in the learning of Logo. This is perhaps not very surprising. However, since the advent of computer use in schools there has been some feeling that it might be possible to develop 'teacher-free' computer applications. Many of the early claims for Logo placed little emphasis on the role of the teacher. More recently, discussion about the learning of Logo has centred around what we see as the false dichotomy between 'telling pupils' and 'discovery learning'. In our view such arguments are only likely to hide the real issues. The computer is a new powerful classroom resource and unless teachers treat it as such and modify their roles accordingly there will be little advantage for pupil learning from its use.

Although our research makes it clear that the teacher's role is important, there is also no doubt that the presence of the computer does change this role. In this chapter we describe teacher strategies found to be effective. Evidence for our conclusions arises from our analysis of the transcript data for the four case study pairs of pupils over the three years of the project. As researchers we had the dual role of both teaching and observing. However, the data collection system of taking videos of each case study session freed us from the need to make detailed notes and the majority of our time in the classroom was spent in a teaching role. We were specifically interested in studying the pupils' developing use of structured programming techniques and pupils' use of variable and our interventions were focused on these two aspects of learning. Previous research had suggested that the learning of these ideas was neither natural nor straightforward (Leron, 1983).

During the first year of research, categories of teacher intervention (Table 9.1) were developed from the transcript data.

Table 9.1 Categories of Intervention

The following categories of intervention were used as a basis for analysis:

MOTIVATIONAL

Reinforcement (R), e.g. 'That's good'
Encouragement (E), e.g. 'Try it'

REFLECTION

Looking Forward (F)
(a) Process (P) Encouraging pupils to reflect on and predict the process.
(b) Goal (G) Encouraging pupils to reflect on their ultimate goal.

Looking Back (LB)
(a) Process (P) Encouraging pupils to reflect back on problem-solving procedures.
(b) Goal (G) Encouraging pupils to reflect on their goal.

DIRECTIONAL Influencing and/or changing the focus of the pupil's attention.

Nudge (N) e.g. 'Do you want to clear the screen?' or 'How about doing your square?'
Method (M) Encouraging pupils to use suitable methods of problem solving (which are already familiar to them).
Building (B) Encouraging pupils to apply a particular piece of previously learned material or knowledge.
Factual (F) (a) New (FN) Supplying a particular piece of new information which is necessary to enable the pupil to continue.
　　　　　 (b) Recall (FR) Reminding pupils of a piece of information (referring them to the handbook).
Powerful Idea (PI) Introducing a 'new powerful idea' or concept, such as procedure, the REPEAT statement or the idea of a variable.
Mathematical Idea (MI) Introducing a new mathematical idea.

These categories were used as a framework for our analysis of the data and for the development of our intervention strategies. At the beginning of the research, our subjective view of the Logo sessions was that we did not intervene very much in the Logo learning and did not unduly influence its development. **Subsequent analysis of the data has shown that this was not the case and pupils' progress in certain areas is closely linked to teacher interventions.** We intervened in the learning process of the pupils by:

- Encouraging pupil control;
- Teacher-devised Tasks;
- Teaching Episodes.

We will consider these separately in the following section.

ENCOURAGING PUPIL CONTROL

We wanted pupils to build up autonomy and reduce their dependence on the teacher and found the following strategies to be important:

- suggestions which were process rather than goal directed;
- comments or follow-up questions which pushed responsibility back to the pupils.

Within this section we discuss our analysis of teacher interventions which kept control with the pupils (see Table 9.1). We divided these interventions into those which were requested by the pupils and those which were initiated by the teacher. A percentage score of interventions within each category was calculated for each pair for each of the three years of the project (Table 9.2). This shows consistency in our way of intervening and reflects our initial decision as to invervention strategies. The majority of the interventions initiated by the teacher were in the category of reflection. Within this category most were categorised as Reflection 'Looking-back process' implying that pupils did not spontaneously reflect back over the processes in which they were engaged.

When we looked at interventions requested by the pupils themselves we found that the majority were of a directional nature suggesting that pupils demanded directional as opposed to meta-cognitive support. The overall number of requested interventions was more than double in the first year of the project than in the third year of the project for all of the pairs. Thus the pupils became less dependent on the teacher and were more likely to resolve a

Table 9.2 Percentage of Interventions Categorised by Motivation, Reflection and Direction (given as percentages of total no. of interventions)

	YEAR 1		YEAR 2		YEAR 3	
	Not Requested	Requested	Not Requested	Requested	Not Requested	Requested
SALLY & JANET						
Motivation	10	1	15	—	8	1
Reflection	43	—	46	1	48	1
Direction	31	15	34	4	37	5
Total	84	16	95	5	93	7
GEORGE & ASIM						
Motivation	14	5	2	3	3	0
Reflection	34	5	66	2	47	0
Direction	24	18	18	9	36	14
Total	72	28	86	14	86	14
LINDA & JUDE/ELAINE						
Motivation	13	1	15	2	8	2
Reflection	36	6	36	1	40	2
Direction	27	17	38	8	41	7
Total	76	24	89	11	89	11
SHAHIDUR & AMANDA/RAVI						
Motivation	—	—	15	5	20	5
Reflection	—	—	36	6	35	6
Direction	—	—	34	4	31	3
Total	—	—	85	15	86	14

problem for themselves. This again supports our overall aim of encouraging pupil autonomy. Although the pupils themselves requested less direction the number of interventions in the category of direction initiated by the teacher remained stable or even increased over the three years of the project. These types of pushes were crucial in provoking pupils to move from a level of actual development towards a level of potential development (Vygotsky, 1978). *P98*

It is worth noting that there was no substantial difference between the proportion of directional interventions given to the pupils who were high mathematical attainers and those who were low mathematical attainers. This was not the case for the proportion of interventions in the category of motivation. By the end of the three years we were intervening more in the category of motivation with the lower attaining pairs (20% in year 3) in comparison to the higher attaining pair (8% for Sally and Janet and 3% for George and Asim). The proportion of motivational interventions may reflect the extent of collaboration between pairs. George and Asim had a proportionally large number of motivational encouragement interventions (16%) compared to the other pairs during their first year, dropping to only 1.5% during the third year when their collaboration self-evidently had improved.

TEACHER-DEVISED TASKS

During the first year of the three-year longitudinal study almost all of the Logo experience was pupil initiated – that is, the pupils were allowed the freedom to work on 'pupil-devised' tasks. This emphasis gradually changed over the period of research. We started to give pupils more 'teacher-devised' tasks in order to:

- encourage pupils to choose from a range of goals;
- confront pupils with a particular programming idea;
- ensure that pupils used appropriate mathematical ideas;
- encourage pupils to use Logo to develop a conceptual framework for new ideas.

It should be mentioned here that even within these task constraints pupils were able to devise their own solution strategies, extend the work as they wished and thus to some extent appropriate the activity for themselves.

Encouraging Pupils to Choose from a Range of Goals

Logo within the mathematics classroom certainly provoked pupils to come up with and struggle with challenging goals of a mathematical nature. During these activities pupils learned to articulate their thoughts and communicate with their partners. Logo provided a problem-solving situation in which mathematical discussion far exceeded that which normally takes place in the mathematics classroom. Pupils were experiencing, probably for the first time, a power to create and be in control of solving their own mathematical problems. Most of the teachers with whom we worked believed that these reasons alone were sufficient to justify Logo programming as an activity in the mathematics classroom.

We recognise the importance from a motivational point of view of the pupils choosing their own goals, and we started our project with a strategy of encouraging this freedom. However, we found that pupils tend to restrict their choice of goal and in so doing restrict the mathematical ideas they are using. In Chapter 4 we discussed the classification of pupil goals along the two separate dimensions:

'Real world' . . . 'Abstract'
Loosely defined . . . Well defined

The discovery that pupils display a strong tendency to work with certain types of goals with different learning outcomes influenced us to intervene to encourage pupils to work from a range of starting points.

Confronting Pupils with a Programming Idea

We found that some pupils chose projects which needed the introduction of the idea of subprocedure and modularity and others did not. In order to provoke pupils to come to appreciate the power of these ideas we introduced several 'teacher-devised' tasks, one of which was the 'SMILE' task (Fig. 9.1) in which the pupils worked in groups of five. The task was aimed at provoking the pupils to *need* to use the idea of subprocedure and to negotiate within the group how each subprocedure should be constructed – each pupil had to do a procedure for one letter. The task asked the pupils to write the word SMILE and then to rearrange their letter procedures to draw *other* words. This latter activity was a crucial part of the task in order that subprocedures – the individual letters – would be perceived by the pupils as useful problem-solving tools in a range of contexts. The task also showed pupils the importance of removing the 'navigating' commands from the 'drawing' commands. In initial attempts interface commands were included in the procedures for each letter. When the letters had to be 'joined' in different ways to construct anagrams of S, M, I, L, E the pupils saw that these interfaces had to be removed and put within separate modules.

We can trace the development of pupils' understanding of subprocedure back to their work on the SMILE task – so it certainly was important. It was time consuming and 'messy' but involved pupils in group work that genuinely *required* collaboration and discussion – about size of letters and how they should be constructed. We printed out the groups' final products – using a floor turtle to emphasise the processes of construction – and were amazed at the variety of anagrams constructed and the variety of methods of construction. Even within the constraints of this task the pupils were able to make the work their own and come up with creative responses.

Another 'teacher-devised' task which we gave the pupils was the 'Variable Squares' task (Fig. 9.2). This task took the form of a game which was played between two pairs of pupils. The aim of the task was to stimulate pupils to consider the similarities in structure between seven figures in order that they might be provoked to use a modular design in their programs – rather than define a new set of square procedures for each figure. The idea for this task was stimulated by some work of Rouchier and Samurçay (1985).

Fig. 9.1 The 'SMILE' Task

SMILE

We have divided you into small groups. Each one in your group should choose one or more letters from the word SMILE. Then write a procedure to draw your chosen letter.

If you choose the letter ⅄⅃ for example it might be helpful if you mark on your letter where the turtle starts and finishes.

When you have all written your procedures put them together in one SUPER procedure which will draw the word SMILE

Then rearrange the letters in a new SUPERPROCEDURE to draw another word.

SLIME   MILES

LIMES

Fig. 9.2 The 'Variable Squares' Task

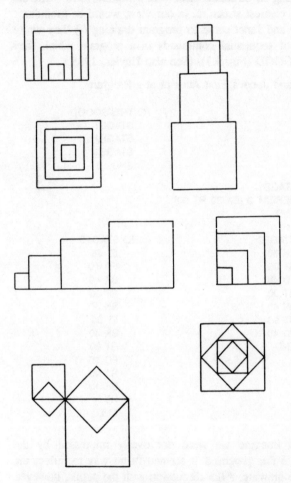

It is well known that there is by no means a 'natural' progression in Logo programming from direct interaction to structured programming (Leron, 1983). As Hillel succinctly put it, 'On the one hand the naturalness of Logo is due to resonances with children's drawing schema but linking programming with drawing stands in the way of making a "procedural analysis" of the task' (Hillel, 1985, p. 88). A communication aspect was built into the 'Variable Squares' task. Each pupil pair was required to communicate their programs to another pair of pupils in their 'team' in such a way that the latter might be able to identify which figure had in fact been

149

drawn. The idea was that each pair would discuss their design with a view to making its structure clear – in symbolic form – for the other pair. The clearest structure, in our view, would be modular.

When Sally and Janet came to program drawing (f) they wrote a long string of sequential commands in a program which they called THISISGOOD (Fig. 9.3). (See also Hoyles, 1985.)

Fig. 9.3 Sally and Janet's First Attempt at a Program

```
TO THISISGOOD
STAGE1
STAGE2
STAGE3
END
```

```
TO STAGE1
REPEAT 3 [BK 20 RT 90]
END
```

```
TO STAGE2
BK 60
RT 90
FD 40
RT 90
BK 40
RT 90
FD 40
END
```

```
TO STAGE3
LT 45
FD 10
BK 40
RT 90
BK 30
LT 90
BK 40
RT 90
FD 10
RT 90
BK 10
HT
END
```

As you might imagine we were not overly impressed by the sophistication of this program! It seemed in no way to reflect the structure of the drawing. After discussion with the pupils, however, we became quickly aware that the program was a result of their interpretation of the social situation at that particular time. They said, for example, 'We will let them have it easier.'

This meant that Sally and Janet thought, *in complete contrast to us*, that a list of sequential commands would be easier to interpret for the other pair than a modular design. They also wanted simply a change since they commented: 'We are fed up with our SQUARE procedure!'

Having heard the remarks we asked them if they could do it 'another way'. With no hesitation or difficulty the pair produced a structured program using a procedure BOX with a variable input! (see Fig. 9.4). When comparing the two programs Sally said, 'That one's quicker (referring to the sequential version) but if you're working it out you can have the boxes . . . !'

Fig. 9.4 Sally and Janet's Second Attempt at a Program

```
TO EASY
    BOX 2
    LT 45
    BOX 1.5
    LT 135
    BOX 1
    LT 45
    BOX .5
    END

TO BOX :SCALE
    FD MUL :SCALE 30
    RT 90
    FD MUL :SCALE 30
    RT 90
    FD MUL :SCALE 30
    RT 90
    FD MUL :SCALE 30
    RT 90
    END
```

Finally, just to make sure that we knew that the structured program was well within their capabilities, they gave it the name – EASY!. This episode showed clearly how careful we must be in making the ideas behind a task clear for pupils and also how tentative we must be in suggesting pupils can or cannot do things. They might merely be following a different agenda from us!

Ensuring that Pupils Use Mathematical Ideas

It is often suggested that Logo is a natural environment for using mathematics. As mathematicians we bring to the Logo situation all our previously learned mathematics and are aware of using these skills and concepts. Pupils, on the other hand, sometimes bring to Logo their mathematical avoidance strategies! For example, we found that pupils often restrict their angle inputs (Chapter 8) to avoid using angles larger than 90° and restrict their choice of number using only multiples of 45 for turtle turn and multiples of 10 for distance (Chapter 8). These self-imposed restrictions can be very pervasive and it seems that collaboration and computer feedback are often not sufficient to 'move' pupils to more generalised or generalisable activity. The use of 'teacher-directed' tasks is helpful – though even when given these, we have found that pupils were quite ingenious at circumventing rather than overcoming obstacles we had carefully placed in their path. We have consequently needed to intervene within pupil activity on a teacher-directed task to nudge pupils beyond their self-constructed boundaries, to use the mathematical ideas they have experienced in other contexts, for example, decimals, and to provoke reflection on this use.

Fig. 9.5 The 'Regular Polygon' Task

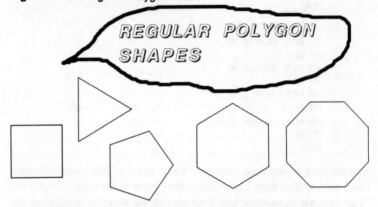

Draw as many of these shapes as possible and fill in the following table

NAME OF SHAPE	NUMBER OF SIDES	TURNING ANGLE
TRIANGLE		
SQUARE	4	
PENTAGON		
HEXAGON		
OCTAGON		45
NONAGON		
DECAGON		

Can you draw a circle?

One of the motivating factors of Logo activity is that pupils can solve a task by using a 'trial and error' perceptual strategy as opposed to using an appropriate mathematical idea in an analytic way. An example of this is that pupils do not necessarily have to use the idea that the 'total turtle turn' is 360 degrees when they are drawing regular polygons. At certain stages during the learning process it is appropriate for pupils to adopt this 'trial and error' approach – so that they become familiar and comfortable with syntax for example. Our work does, however, suggest that pupils are not likely to spontaneously adopt analytic strategies and discover the relationship between the number of sides and the turtle turn for a regular polygon for themselves. We prepared a 'teacher-devised' task (Fig. 9.5) to specifically confront pupils with this idea. A detailed description of Panos and John's involvement in this task is presented in Chapter 8.

Using Logo to Develop a Conceptual Framework for Mathematical Ideas

Our research has been concerned with secondary school pupils and it is inevitable that these pupils bring with them a large 'baggage' of previously learned mathematics – often including many mathematical 'misconceptions'. Most of the case study pupils, however, had no previous experience of the concept of variable before the start of the Logo activity. Thus for these pupils, the Logo context provided their first experience of using a variable to represent a range of numbers and writing an abstract formulation for a generalised rule. We found that pupils very rarely chose goals for themselves which *needed* the idea of variable and so devised a 'teacher-directed' task (Fig. 12.1) to introduce pupils to the potential of variable. After being introduced to the idea of variable in this context many of the pupils did subsequently initiate the idea of using variable within their own goals. Chapter 12 describes in detail the way we intervened to provoke pupils to use and understand variable in Logo and to make links between the ideas in Logo and the ideas in 'paper and pencil' algebra.

We can now see the potential of using Logo to devise microworlds for other areas of the mathematics curriculum; for example, ratio and proportion, number, graphs, trigonometry vectors. The idea is to design activities both on and off the computer where pupils will naturally use a new mathematical idea and by this use – together with appropriate teacher intervention – debug any misconceptions and then differentiate and generalise its attributes. We are now developing these microworlds in conjunction with mathematics teachers as part of a programme of research and inservice education (Hoyles, Noss and Sutherland, 1986).

TEACHING EPISODES

We found on analysis of our transcript data that when a programming idea was introduced to the pupils the nature of our intervention tended to change and the teacher, rather than the pupil, became in control of the interaction. We labelled such sequences of interactions as teaching episodes. Our intervention categories (Table 9.1) were not appropriate for the classification of interaction within these teaching episodes. Very often such episodes occurred at the end of a session under the pressure of 'the bell'. They tended to reflect our 'hidden agenda' for a session – that is, what we had set out to 'teach' but had not found an opportunity to introduce in the context of the pupils' own goals. Analysis of the teaching episodes also shows that they frequently served to introduce the pupils to Logo structures and syntax – that is, to help the pupils build a formalisation of their activity. We now recognise the crucial importance of trying to bridge the gap between pupil actions and their formalisation and the role Logo can play in this endeavour – provided of course that appropriate symbolic structures are introduced.

The pupils' way of solving a problem was often unexpected and in the early stages of the project we sometimes made the mistake of imposing a Logo formalism on the pupils which matched *our* problem solution rather than *their* problem solution. For example, Sally and Janet had defined procedures for six regular polygons all of the form illustrated in the following program for a pentagon:

```
TO PENT
    REPEAT 4 [FD 50 RT 72]
    FD 50
    END
```

It seemed appropriate at this point to introduce the girls to a procedure for a general regular polygon *but* the structure chosen followed a standard form rather than the pupils' constructions:

```
TO POLY :N
    REPEAT :N [FD 50 RT DIV 360 :N]
    END
```

154

We found that this type of intervention, in which the teacher's imposed Logo structure did not match the pupils' own problem solution, often introduced unnecessary confusion for the pupils – as their activity did not connect with its formalisation, with the result that the latter had no semantic meaning. Such episodes were also associated with a lowering of motivation and an absence of task involvement.

As the project progressed we learned to match the 'teacher-given' Logo structure and syntax to the pupils' own solution, as the following example illustrates.

Sally and Janet had written a procedure to draw a variable-sized pine tree and used this in direct drive to draw a row of pine trees (Fig. 9.6a) by entering the commands: MOVE1, PINE 120, MOVE2, PINE 110, MOVE3, PINE 100 etc. They wanted to write a superprocedure called FOREST but Janet did not want to have to type all the commands in again.

Janet	'Instead of typing all this out . . . how are we going to make a big program?'
Sally	'But we can't, 'cos we can't just type REPEAT MOVE1 PINE 120 'cos it's just going to keep on the same one all the time isn't it?'
Janet	'Yeah . . . but . . . yeah, I know, but . . . is there any way we could do . . . ?No, I didn't think so . . . '
Sally	'Miss, is there any way you know how you do REPEAT it . . . so it won't do the same thing all the time?'

The intervention was requested. It was a cue for us to introduce the idea of recursion – which simply provided the structure for 'capturing' their hands-on activity.

Intervention	'Now, so imagine you're here at the end and you want to do your row . . . now what you want to do is you want it to do PINE with a value, say SIDE, and then you want it to do MOVE2 and then you want it to do PINE again . . . what's the next value?'
Janet	'110'
Intervention	'If the first one was PINE the value of side what's the value of the next PINE?'
Sally	'Minus 10'
Intervention	'Minus 10 from side, so if you'd done 110 from

side then you do PINE again with minus 10 from side ... so what you want to do is do PINE with a value of side and then you do MOVE and then you do FOREST. Do a copy of FOREST ... this is quite hard and you want to subtract 10 off the side ... now do you see what that does? First of all it does PINE with the value of side you put in it, you move and then it does it all again ... FOREST. Now what does FOREST do? It does PINE with a value of 10 less and it does MOVE then it gets to the bottom of here and it calls another copy of itself so it does PINE 10 less ... so it's going to go on and on and on and on, do you understand? ... This is called recursion, so it starts and then it does itself again but instead of having side it does it with 10 less than side.'

The following procedure was written:

Fig 9.6 The 'Row of Pines' Task

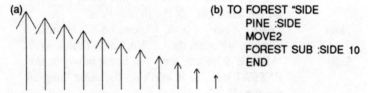

(a)

(b) TO FOREST "SIDE
        PINE :SIDE
        MOVE2
        FOREST SUB :SIDE 10
        END

We suggest that teaching episodes, in which the Logo syntax and structure matched the pupils' own solution, contributed to the learning of the pupils. However, because teaching episodes cannot be carefully planned it is inevitable that this matching does not always take place, which can be both alienating and confusing for pupils. We now believe that it would be preferable to be more explicit about what we aim for the pupils to learn from a series of Logo sessions and plan 'teacher-devised' tasks specifically to achieve these learning outcomes. Such tasks would reduce (though not eliminate) the need for teaching episodes and would allow pupils to retain control of their learning under teacher guidance.

IMPLICATIONS FOR CLASSROOM PRACTICE

The majority of our teacher interventions over the three-year period of the longitudinal study concerned structured programming, making generalisations or using the idea of variable to formalise a generalisation. We made very few interventions concerning the details of local planning related to, for example, angle calculation or estimation of distances. From our analysis of the data we see a clear development in all the pupils as far as the ideas of structured programming and variable are concerned (Chapters 5 and 12). Their development of understanding of angle and total turn is not so uniform across all the case study pairs (Chapter 8). This suggests that if we allow pupils to learn Logo 'naturally' without interventions from the teacher focused on specific learning outcomes then what individual pupils actually learn will vary considerably. It also appears that the pupils who are not attaining well in their 'normal' mathematics are likely to be the most disadvantaged in such circumstances. We are not saying that these pupils need more direction in the form of 'telling' but that they need more support in terms of building bridges between Logo and 'paper and pencil' mathematics and overcoming Logo misconceptions (Chapter 7). In addition, their self-esteem and self-confidence is likely to benefit from their being allowed the freedom to work towards their own goals.

The main implications of this chapter for teaching and learning are:

- the importance of interventions to provoke the pupils to reflect on process – in terms of prediction and 'looking back';
- the importance of establishing a teacher-pupil relationship in which the pupils learn to assert control of the computing activity and do not turn to the teacher for the 'right answer' or the 'right method';
- the importance of matching the 'teacher-given' Logo formalism to the pupils' negotiated problem solution;
- the recognition that when pupils work in pairs the need for teacher intervention to motivate the pupils is usually decreased;
- the recognition that if pupils choose their own goals this increases pupil motivation and engagement in the task but can restrict the range of mathematical ideas used by the pupils. To counterbalance this, pupils also need to work on 'teacher-devised' tasks designed for specific learning outcomes.

Our work during the Logo Maths Project has suggested ways we can profitably intervene in the pupils' programming activity to aid mathematical learning. How to structure the situation without taking the control away from the pupils and without inhibiting exploratory activities is a question for which we are only beginning to find answers. We know on the one hand that we must sometimes carefully organise the pupils' learning environment, yet we have observed pupils losing motivation because of 'over-intervention'. Teachers must decide on the aims of the Logo activity in their classrooms and then base their intervention strategies around these aims. Somehow a balance must be found between allowing pupils the freedom to work on their own extended projects and structuring the activity for specific learning outcomes – to avoid 'gaps' in pupils' awareness of the potential use of Logo and to confront any misconceptions. We feel that perhaps one way forward is to devise tasks *but* allow the pupils to make the decision as to procedures for solution.

ACKNOWLEDGEMENT

A modified version of this chapter has appeared in Mandl *et al.*, 1988.

10

Gender Issues

INTRODUCTION

It is a matter of grave concern that our culture is defining computers as pre-eminently male machines. Despite the fact that in everyday life computers are becoming ubiquitous the use of the computer in education seems to be following the traditional lines of gender bias in society. The present situation raises distinctly familiar questions of equity in terms of access to and use of technology. While girls and boys might show similar appreciation of the significance computers might have for their personal futures, boys tend to be more positively disposed towards computers than girls, are more likely to take optional computer courses in school than girls, to report more frequent home use of computers than girls and moreover tend to dominate the limited computer resources that are available in school. It is also the case that even when girls are able to obtain access to the machines in school only a restricted set of activities (which exclude programming for example) are often deemed to be appropriate for them. Finally, few girls take up any employment using computer skills (other than data processing or word processing).

It is therefore difficult to avoid the disturbing conclusion that girls are learning less about computers and therefore acquiring less understanding as to how computers might be used for their own purposes. A basic premise underlying this chapter is that gender differences in attitude to and competence with computers are neither inevitable nor immutable. Differences which have emerged arise from a variety of sources. First they arise from the social image of computers which reveal how deeply-held 'default assumptions', of which we are hardly aware, permeate our mental

159

representations. Such assumptions, described by Hofstadter (1985), are illustrated in the following story.

A father and his son were driving to a ball game when their car stalled on the railroad tracks. In the distance a train whistle blew a warning. Frantically, the father tried to start the engine, but in his panic, he couldn't turn the key, and the car was hit by the onrushing train. An ambulance sped to the scene and picked them up. On the way to the hospital, the father died. The son was still alive but his condition was very serious, and he needed immediate surgery. The moment they arrived at the hospital, he was wheeled into an emergency operating room, and the surgeon came in, expecting a routine case. However, on seeing the boy, the surgeon blanched and muttered, 'I can't operate on this boy – he's my son.'

Hofstadter points out that to most of us, '... bizarre worlds with such things as reincarnation come more easily to mind than the idea that a surgeon could be a woman!' (Hofstadter, 1985, p. 139). In a similar way controlling computers tends to call up a default image. Differences between males' and females' relationships to computers also relate to the particular uses that computers have been put; for example the treatment of a computer merely as a 'topic' or object of knowledge has serious educational consequences for girls. This leads on to the general question of access to computers and the time made available for computer experience. When there is competition over scarce resources, girls tend to 'lose out' and this has certainly been observed in relation to computers in schools. However, analysis that only examines forces that push girls away from the computers oversimplifies gender inequality issues. We must look beyond an essentially transitional situation dominated by shortage of hardware and software. *If it is true that experience with computers in school is crucial then we must consider what type of experiences should be made available and how they should be organised.* There is a need for attention to be paid to the cognitive style associated with computer use, the type of software used and the ways computers have been organised and supported in classrooms.

One crucial factor in considering computer use is mode of working. The use of the computer is often seen as isolating and devoid of interaction with others. We must allow flexible working arrangements which cater for peer collaboration as well as for individual work. This then raises questions of effective working partnerships. It also raises questions as to what is valued by teachers. Carmichael et al. (1986), found that boys loved to work fast to complete the challenges set but the girls lost interest as their efforts were not acknowledged. One girl commented, 'Boys get commended for things that girls can do, but we complete it half an hour later, and it doesn't matter then' (quoted in Moore, 1986, p. 7). Another factor is the sex of the teacher and the availability of female role models. Girls need to see females as competent, confident and enthusiastic computer users ... although of course it must be recognised that the sex of the teacher is not a predictor of non-sexist practice!

PROGRAMMING

In a useful summary of research into the use of computers in schools, Lockheed distinguishes three different computer applications: the computer as an object of study (programming, computer studies or computer literacy courses); the computer as recreation (game playing), and the computer as a general purpose tool (word processing, database management, spreadsheets, graphics, music generation, and so forth) (Lockheed, 1985, p. 119). She points out that males use computers more than females for programming and game playing but not more for other computer applications. This finding in relation to programming is also mentioned in a recent survey of 1,747 teenagers in the UK (Fife-Shaw, Breakwell, Lee and Spencer, 1986) who showed that boys used computers substantially more than girls did and that the sex difference was particularly strong for 'high-level' activities such as programming.

We have argued in this book that programming can have an educationally beneficial influence on the nature and content of school mathematics. We would also argue therefore that the exclusion of programming from the computer activities available to girls reinforces sex stereotyping of girls. Although some forms of computer interaction may leave one feeling comfortable, if there is no feeling of *power* or *control* over the computer (which comes with some sort of programming) there will *not* be a sense of computer competence or confidence.

If we are now to consider programming in schools we have to look carefully at what this means and what implications it might have for girls. By focusing on gender specific behaviour and attitudes in this way we recognise that we are overlooking important individual differences. What we want to do is highlight a

161

distinction between two modes of thought and styles of learning rather than represent a generalisation about either sex. Dirckinck-Holmfeld (1985) argues that 'data logics' are essentially alien to the female form of cognition because of social and cultural influences. Here 'data logics' means the translation of actions into a logical, linear and unambiguous language. She suggests that for such a translation to take place, the problem must essentially have already been solved. A mechanistic form of thinking which devalues the role of intuition during the process of problem solution may therefore be encouraged. If programming is viewed in this narrow way, that is in a way which emphasises planning and logical progression, it undoubtedly will alienate pupils with different preferred learning styles. Yet there *are* different yet valid approaches to programming. Computer programming is not *necessarily* an activity which imposes a linear planning style (this is what is termed 'hard mastery' by Turkle, 1984). Many programmers are 'soft' masters. Soft masters interact with the computer and work on a problem by arranging and rearranging the elements within it rather than carrying out a preworked plan. By this method they often come up with new and surprising results. It is the case that many expert programmers use this negotiating style whenever they tackle something new. The point to be made here is that there are different programming styles and girls may favour the more soft approach.

The programming language used obviously has a crucial influence on the style adopted by the programmer. The computer language Logo, because of its structured and procedural nature, is particularly encouraging to soft mastery. Logo can provide a new way of building a relationship with computational objects and formal systems since these objects can be named, explored and manipulated. However, even whilst using a computer language such as Logo, we must recognise the overriding influence of what is valued and assessed in the classroom. Carmichael et al. (1986) in reporting research on the use of Logo found large variations in performance between boys and girls (in favour of boys). These performance variations were based on a series of test results and a content analysis of the amount and variety of work saved. Although it was suggested that these results were primarily a function of the amount of time students were able to engage with Logo, the whole issue of the type of work which made up the performance criteria needs to be addressed. For example, in discussing variety of work, Carmichael et al. reported that the girls tended to stay with the ideas they knew and with which they were familiar. Girls were viewed in a rather negative way as being thorough, methodical, and aiming for perfection. In contrast, the work of the boys was reported in positive tones as being innovative and experimental. Boys, it was said, explored many more Logo primitives, were eager to make their own games (frequently combining text and graphics in the process) and discovered new ways of creating movement on the screen. Competence in programming was therefore assessed by acquaintance with a large number of commands, by the complexity of programs developed, and by the completion of challenges. Depth of understanding and creativity in the multiple uses of a small number of commands did not appear to be valued so highly.

As acknowledged by Carmichael et al. in their concluding remarks, this type of assessment of programming skills can bias the appeal of computers. Programming, which stresses rules and winning, would tend to be incompatible with socialised female values (such as relational ethics) as pointed out by Gilligan (1982). An objective/subjective polarisation then becomes a masculine/ feminine polarisation where the feminine approach is devalued (see also Nielson, 1987). Thus if we emphasise challenges and individual mastery we must first recognise that girls may suffer negative emotional reactions (for example, fear of success at the expense of others). More fundamentally we must also acknowledge that we are *imposing* a cognitive style which emphasises the separation of self from object. Papert (1986) argued that some individuals prefer to work by *identifying with* objects and contextualising knowledge through this identification. These people prefer to break down the barriers between self and object in order to work inside the situation rather than 'plan, freeze the plan and then execute the plan'. We would argue that these different styles of working do not affect the quality of the result. Care must be taken, therefore, not to assess performance in ways that *assume a particular approach*. In addition we must look to the distribution of topics we choose to assess. In the particular area of computing it has been reported by Anderson (1987) that 'High school females performed better than males in *specific areas of programming* (our emphasis) . . . such as problem analysis and algorithmic application . . . ' and concluded that 'computer tests . . . should be carefully examined . . . for bias against women and minorities and for bias against non-mathematical computer work' (p. 50). We come now to the fundamental issue. We question the widely held assumption that the way to be a successful programmer and problem solver is to exhibit what are termed autonomous learning behaviours (Fennema *et al.*, 1985). Such behaviours emphasise independent mastery over formal knowledge. We argue that girls and women may find this style of work alienating. *Yet* they *are* quite able to think and talk about formal systems if a different approach is taken. We now turn to the results of the Logo Maths Project research as illustration of these general points.

SOME FINDINGS

In the Logo Maths Project attention was paid to social and contextual issues such as modes of working and cognitive style. No gender differences were observed in terms of motivation, setting of challenging goals, persistence, showing initiative and anxiety about the computer as a machine. Girls have enjoyed the collaborative atmosphere and excelled at 'pattern spotting' and seeing the structure underlying a program or problem. There has also been some indication of a change in teacher perception of the girls. After the Logo work, girls were more likely to be seen as having potential for creative problem solving. This may be because the girls actually changed their behaviour or it may be that the teacher merely saw them differently – in either way it is of significance.

In addition to the above general points, by the end of the three years of the project we found no evidence of any differences between girls and boys with respect to their:

* ability to use the ideas of structured programming when working on a well-defined task;
* ability to use the ideas of variable;
* facility with a 'top-down' or 'bottom-up' approach to planning.

We will now discuss how the issue of gender affects the learning situation in terms of:

* ways of interacting with the computer;
* collaboration and discussion between pupil pairs;
* attitude to mode of working.

Ways of Interacting with the Computer

Types of goal and differences in emphasis. At the beginning of the Logo Maths Project as discussed in earlier chapters the pupils were given the freedom to choose their own goals and develop their own problem-solving and programming strategies. Researcher interventions aimed to focus on process and to encourage the pupils to predict and reflect. We did not impose any 'idealised' problem-solving strategies on the pupils as we wanted to investigate the different ways pupils would naturally work at the computer. We carried out an analysis of the types of goals on which pupils chose to work. These goals were classified along a dimension concerned with the extent to which the pupils defined and planned the final outcome of their work. We labelled the extremes of this dimension, loosely-defined/well-defined goals (as described in Chapter 4). When pupils were given the freedom to choose their own goals they exhibited preferences for certain types of projects and these preferences seem to reflect a gender differentiation. Our research data indicates that girls more often chose loosely-defined goals and boys more often chose well-defined goals when programming in the turtle graphics subset of Logo as illustrated in Table 10.1.

Table 10.1 Ratio of Loosely-defined to Well-defined Goals for the Case Study Pupils

	Loosely Defined	Well Defined
Girl Pairs	22	1
Boy Pairs	5	21
Girl/Boy Pairs	14	11

We suggest that in our school culture the more well-defined a goal appears to be the more value it is accorded. School culture reflects our production-oriented society. Girls' apparent lack of emphasis on product can easily lead to their work being undervalued. This was mentioned earlier with reference to the Carmichael *et al.* (1985) project where it was reported that 'without exception the boys saved more programs than the girls'. We would argue that this focus on product and quantity not only reflects a bias in performance criteria but also would tend to emphasise a certain type of learning.

165

Carmichael described how the girls tended to stay with the ideas they knew and with which they were familiar, giving as an example one pair of girls who spent most of the first year working with circles, 'filling them with different colours and combining them to make lollipops and balloons'. We too have observed a similar phenomenon but do not make the same negative value judgement of such explorations since they are important for certain aspects of learning. For example, we have evidence that the girls through their extensive work on loosely-defined goals were more able later to break down well-defined tasks into modules. Well-defined projects on the other hand were more likely to provoke pupils to attend to the detail of turtle turn and make links between angle and turtle turn. This point is again echoed by Carmichael et al. who found that boys were more likely than girls to know the size of the angle needed in a turtle graphics project. We would interpret this result as a consequence of the type of activity experienced.

All the extended network pupils in the Logo Maths Project were given paper and pencil Logo tasks at the end of the project. From one of these tasks (the 'K' task, Fig. 10.1) we again have evidence that the boys were more likely to have made the links between turtle turn and angle. Almost twice as many boys as girls traced out correctly RT 135 for the 'K' task. In the 'M' debugging task (Fig. 10.2) more girls than boys modified the correct command; that is, understood the sequence although making an incorrect modification. There is also evidence from these tasks that the boys are focusing more on the object itself and are not so much concerned with the initial orientation of the turtle before it starts to draw. In the 'H' task, which involved asking the pupils to draw a figure from a list of commands, 11% of boys as opposed to 3% of girls drew the correct figure without bothering with initial orientation. Similarly in the 'F' task which involved asking the pupils to write a procedure to draw the letter F, 14% of boys as opposed to 3% of girls gave a correct solution apart from the initial orientation of the turtle. In contrast girls seem more likely to focus on the relationship between objects on the screen and are more likely to define subprocedures for the interface commands which join two graphical objects. More research is needed in order to substantiate these claims.

Fig. 10.1 The 'K' Task

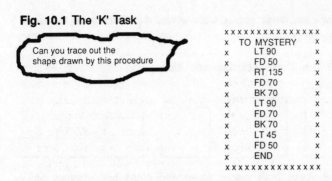

Can you trace out the shape drawn by this procedure

```
x x x x x x x x x x x x x x x
x   TO MYSTERY      x
x     LT 90         x
x     FD 50         x
x     RT 135        x
x     FD 70         x
x     BK 70         x
x     LT 90         x
x     FD 70         x
x     BK 70         x
x     LT 45         x
x     FD 50         x
x     END           x
x x x x x x x x x x x x x x x
```

Fig. 10.2 The 'M' Debugging Task

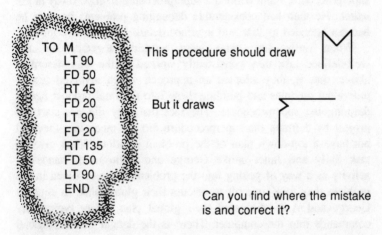

```
TO M
  LT 90
  FD 50
  RT 45
  FD 20
  LT 90
  FD 20
  RT 135
  FD 50
  LT 90
  END
```

This procedure should draw

But it draws

Can you find where the mistake is and correct it?

Differences in approach to the same well-defined problem.
Throughout the Logo Maths Project we occasionally gave the longitudinal case study pupils either individually or in pairs the same well-defined task. We have observed differences in programming style between the girls and the boys. These differences cannot be adequately described by reference to the dimension of 'top-down' planner and 'bottom-up' planner but are more to do with mode of computer interaction (as described in Chapters 4 and 5). In fact one boy and one girl, Asim and Sally, both tended to be 'top-down' planners whereas George and Janet both tended to be 'bottom-up' planners. In contrast to Asim though, Sally always wanted to work initially in direct mode. Her behaviour masked the fact that she nearly always started a project with a clear 'top-down' plan.

167

All the case study pupils were given the 'Decreasing Squares' task (Fig. 10.3).

Fig. 10.3 The 'Decreasing Squares' Task

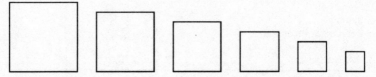

Sally and Asim both made 'top-down' plans but whereas Sally tested all the modules of her 'top-down' plan and then used these to build up the row of decreasing squares *before* defining the final superprocedure, Asim defined a superprocedure *straight away in the editor*. He then had considerable debugging problems because he had not attended to state and interface details in his square module.

When Sally and Janet were working together on any well-defined task they consistently worked in the way described above, that is, they adopted an approach which involved testing individual modules and building these into the final product *before* defining the superprocedure. The fact that they did not start the project by defining the superprocedure did *not* mean that they did not have a top-down plan of the problem solution. When given a task Sally and Janet unlike George and Asim used 'hands-on' activity as a way of getting into the problem. Once involved in the problem they took time off to discuss their global plan. In contrast George and Asim discussed their global plan *before* typing any commands into the computer. There is the danger that superficial observation could lead to the conclusion that Sally and Janet were not planning. Our evidence suggests that they do plan when working towards well-defined goals but the nature of their interaction with the computer is different from the boys. They use interaction with the computer to get started and to engage in the problem. Table 10.2 illustrates the comparisons described above by reference to the type of programming activity undertaken, the number of utterances of the pupils and the number of computer commands used.

Table 10.2(a) Task Analysis for Sally and Janet's 'Arrow' Task

Type of Programming Activity	No. of Utterances	No. of Computer Commands
Planning	2	0
'Hands-on'	27	21
Planning	44	2
Defining a procedure	10	24
'Hands-on' (trying out a procedure which works)	3	6

Table 10.2(b) Task Analysis for George and Asim's 'Arrow' Task

Type of Programming Activity	No. of Utterances	No. of Computer Commands
Planning	22	2
'Hands-on'	10	8
Refining plan and negotiating syntax	51	0
'Hands-on'	12	1
Defining a procedure	7	6
'Hands-on' (trying out a procedure which has a small bug)	4	1
Debugging	1	1
'Hands-on' (trying out a procedure which works)	8	9

These differences observed for our case study pupils have also been found in the extended network data. Boys were more likely than girls to 'jump in' at too high a level, in terms of defining a procedure in the editor when they did not have a clear idea of the process within the procedure. This often led to difficulties in debugging. For example, all the extended network pupils were given the task of drawing a row of four identical squares at the end of their first year and second year of Logo programming (as described in Chapter 5). Analysis of the data showed that whereas there was no difference between the number of boys and the number of girls who obtained a working program, there were considerably more boys than girls who wrote procedures which they then could not subsequently debug.

Pupils' choice of variable names. Another unexpected difference between boys and girls concerned their choice of variable names. It had been observed at an early stage that pupils were attaching too much significance to meaningful variable names like SIDE

169

and NUM. Using a wide range of variable names, including 'nonsense' names, was considered to be an indication that pupils understood that in Logo any variable name could be used. In analysing the range of variable names used by the pupils it was found that not only did girls choose to use a much wider range of names but they were also more likely to be imaginative in their choice of names. The names chosen by George and Janet throughout the three years of the project are given below to serve as an example of this point.

Names chosen by Janet. NUMBER, NUM, SIDE, SCALE, N, D, E, K, M, J, X, R, YT, HT, RAD, TWA, ONE, TWO, JACK, JILL, CAT, WO, MAN, NUT, IT, ORE, JOE, LEE, PIG

Names chosen by George. NUM, SCALE, LEN, LEN2, NUT, SIDE1, SIDE2, AREA1, AREA2, DISTANCE, ANGLE, X, Y, B, O, DIG

When Janet solved the 'Arrow' task (Fig. 10.4) she used the variable names JACK and JILL and when George solved the task he used the variable names NUT and NUM. Both solutions were equally sophisticated from both a programming and a mathematical point of view.

We also found that the freedom to use any variable name (and any procedure name) provided a motivating factor for the girls when they were working on a task which involved defining simple functions in Logo – the girls enjoyed the creative side of choosing a name. The following are examples of functions defined by girl pairs:

```
TO HAZEL :NUT                          equivalent to x → x/3
    OUTPUT DIV :NUT 3
    END

TO POXIE :SEAN                         equivalent to y → y – 17
    OUTPUT SUB :SEAN 17
    END
```

The imaginative choice of variable names in no way changes the mathematical structure of the procedures and quite obviously contributed to the pupils' engagement in the task. The boys did not appear to want to use variable names in the same way and were more likely to write procedures in the following form:

```
TO ASIM :P              equivalent to z → 3z
    OUTPUT MUL 3 :P
    END
```

We are not attempting to put any differential value on either nonsense names (for example SEAN) or abstract names (for example P) but it is worth considering that in the 'normal' mathematics context pupils are usually restricted to abstract names. We suggest that for the girls the free choice of variable names in the Logo context adds an additional motivating factor to the mathematical activity.

Collaboration and Discussion between Pupil Pairs

Gender differences were observable in the nature of interaction between pupil pairs, with a girl being consciously more likely to share with her partner her representation of the problem and her ideas for problem solution.

Fig. 10.4 The 'Arrow' Task

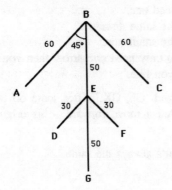

(Note: The lengths and letters were not included on the original task).

MAKE A PROCEDURE TO DRAW THIS SHAPE AS BIG OR AS SMALL AS YOU WISH.

Let us take some selected interactions during work on the 'Arrow' task (Fig. 10.4) as an illustration of the above points. We shall focus on the processes by which the pupils, working collaboratively, negotiated how they saw the task and developed a plan as to how their goal might be achieved. For both pairs the

171

coding of the pupil utterances (Appendix 2) indicated a high overall level of elaborated argument. The episode for the two girls is described in Chapter 7. Let us contrast the girls' interaction with those of George and Asim when given the same task. First of all it was apparent that the two boys *saw the task differently*. George saw it as being made up of two parts ABCE *placed on top of* DEFG, while Asim saw it purely as one arrow superimposed on another arrow half its size. From the first section of the transcript, it is clear that neither boy was willing to change his representation and accommodate his partner's view. So they essentially worked out individual plans which then came into conflict when the pair had to agree on a Logo program. In addition, the figure the boys worked towards did not reflect the ratios of the lengths given but were the same as those perceived by the girls.

The boys drew DEFG in direct mode. With the turtle at E the discussion showed that they had not agreed on an overall view of the task. The nature of their discussion did not help them to achieve a consensus.

Asim	'Just draw an arrow and MUL it.'
George	'Go forward the same distance.'
Asim	'But you only need one.'
George	'No, these are the same distance.'
Asim	'What? That's the small one.'
George	'I know, but you only need one arrow then you can MUL it as you like.'

George apparently agreed and said 'Oh, OK.' After some off-task talk, however, he again suggested a move forward – his original plan.

George	'FD 20, 'cos that's always the same.'
Asim	'No it isn't.'
George	'It is.'
Asim	'No it isn't.'
George	'It is, 'cos that's the same distance as that.'
Asim	'Yeh, but if we ... '

Even though there was no consensus George started to type FORWARD ... Asim reverted to an authority figure, i.e. the teacher, to try to settle the dispute.

Asim	'Go on, ask her if what we are going to be drawing afterwards is that or the whole thing.'

George	'I know, 'cos that is always going to be the same.'
Asim	'Which one?'
George	'That FD 20.'
Asim	'I know, that's what I mean. That's why I have to check up.'
George	'It is always the same, I know that.'
George	'The FD 20, 'cos that is always the same distance.'
Asim	'I know, but it depends on whether you're going to be drawing if you're going like that or if you're going to be drawing an arrow there, an arrow there...'
George	'It's still always the same.'
Asim	'If you're wrong I'll kill you, go on.'

This style of interaction was reflected throughout the session. Disagreements tended to be resolved by reference to an outside authority. The boys (unlike the girls) also spent a lot of time discussing syntax but again could not agree and eventually asked the teacher.

Asim	'BK two dots MUL.'
George	'No, it's not. No, BK NUM.'
Asim	'10, no you don't put MUL ... you only put NUM ... it's got nothing to do with MUL. It'll be NUM two dots 10.'
George	'No, it's backward 10. Multiplied by 2 each time. No, it's BK two dots NUM.'
Asim	'That's what I keep saying. Why don't you listen to me and then you put 10 afterwards or 10 before it?'
George	'Ask Miss.'

Even though George continued with his idea, Asim was still not convinced and when they came eventually to write a procedure definition, he again remarked:

Asim	'What I want to understand, OK, is that is this arrow supposed to be one arrow like that ... forget about the top, or is it supposed to be like that or is it supposed to be like that?'
George	'Like that.'
Asim	'Or is it supposed to be a whole thing?'

George   'Yeah. That, that, that, that . . . '

Asim   'They're supposed to be together.'

As mentioned earlier the boys *did* take on each other's ideas, although their language and combative style made it seem that they did not. This is illustrated in the following extract.

George pointed out at the beginning of the episode that the initial orientation of the turtle was not important (as the Arrow was to be a completely general procedure).

George   'Actually we can't have that LT 90 there because if we do that every time we do arrow it will go . . . '

Much later when the boys were at the point of building their procedure, it was Asim who took up this point. They had entered the editor when Asim said:

Asim   'What is it, LT 90? There isn't any point in turning round, is there?'

George   'But I'm just turning it upwards.'

Asim   'There's no need to do that, remember?'

It turned out, however, that George was planning ahead – although he had not yet disclosed this to Asim! He realised that given the way they had constructed their program (in a modular way with two calls of ARROW with a centre CT in between (see below)) they had to think of turtle orientation after all!

George   'There *is* a need . . . if you do that and centre it again you have to turn it again.'

They therefore introduced an input, NUT, to their procedure which oriented each call of ARROW in the same way:

```
TO ARROWPLUS :NUT
   LT :NUT
   ARROW 20
   CT
   LT :NUT
   ARROW 40
   END
```

The differences found in our overall analysis which are illustrated in the above examples are very similar to those of Nielsen and Roepstorf (1985) who reported that

'The girls tend to orient themselves towards each other. The human relation seems equally – or more important – than the object they are working with. They seem to operate within a we-circle, and the cooperation is predominantly collective. The boys apparently work more individually, and orient themselves primarily towards the object, and secondarily, but also essential, towards each other. Though with attitudes which are different from those of the girls, the boys also cooperate, but the dominant tendency is towards an individual performance, often with what we have termed an element of competition. . . .Whether or not the individual girl was capable of solving the posed problem, or knew the next step, she most often drew the other girl into a collective cooperation by using verbal suggestions like: "Don't you think . . . " or "What if we turned it more?". Whether or not the other girl agreed, the suggestion was very often made the object of a discussion, in which mathematical concepts were used only tentatively' (p. 65).

Thus the girls were less likely to fight for control than the boys – who often seemed concerned to establish their autonomy and impose their problem representation and solution. Boys used few verbal supports of their partner's contributions. They appeared to be trying hard to convince each other, which led to a competitive style of speech. Boys tended to be more careful with the exact local detail of their designs, which were often very carefully planned in advance. Their interactions were therefore often simply suggestions for actions which were not negotiable as they had already been worked out in advance. This type of verbal interaction is obviously related to the boys' tendency to choose well-defined goals. It might be easy to interpret from the boys' language that they do not collaborate or listen to each other's suggestions as their final actions often appear to be based on 'who was the strongest or most persistent'. In fact we have found frequent cases when ideas from a partner were taken up later – but *not* acknowledged!

Attitude to Mode of Working

An attitude to mathematics questionnaire was administered to all pupils (total 222) in the extended network schools in order to explore the effects of working with Logo. In considering gender differences we will focus on two of the results from this questionnaire data. In response to the item 'I enjoy working with others in the class' the responses of the girls over the period of the research became increasingly more positive. Initially the response of the girls to this item was less positive than boys while at the end of the project the reverse was the case.

The response to the following item also showed interesting gender differences.

'When I get stuck on a maths problem:
(A) I like to try and work it out for myself.
(B) I ask someone else in the class to help me.
(C) I ask the teacher.
(D) All three on different occasions.'

Boys consistently were more likely to state a preference (A), for 'working it out on their own'. Very few boys ticked response (B). In contrast girls were more ambivalent in their responses but exhibited an increase in the response (B) over the period of the research.

In interviews with the individual pupils, preferred working mode – individual or with other – was probed further. Girls who expressed a liking for group work emphasised the importance of receiving help from their peers. Boys in contrast saw group work as distracting from their individual achievements. Boys who preferred individual work focused on the individual challenge involved and the opportunity for being able to puzzle things out for themselves without arguments from peers. Girls, in contrast, who liked individual work emphasised how they could progress at their own pace.

IMPLICATIONS FOR CLASSROOM PRACTICE

In conclusion we wish to reiterate a point made earlier in this chapter – that is, by our focus on gender specific behaviour and attitudes we recognise that we are ignoring important individual variations. None the less, by adopting this focus we have been able to distinguish different styles of learning and modes of interaction with the computer. In our analysis, we have been aware of the danger of coming to quick and superficial conclusions. Consideration of individual episodes or short-term performance results can sometimes be misleading, and it is all too easy to come up with slogans such as 'Girls do not plan and boys do not collaborate in their computer work' or 'Boys are better than girls in programming'. We have confidence in our interpretations because they are backed up by systematic, longitudinal data and we have found, not surprisingly, that the situation is far more complex than this – girls *do* plan and boys *do* collaborate but not necessarily in the way we would predict, and who achieves more is at least partly dependent on how we organise and assess the activity.

ACKNOWLEDGEMENTS

A modified version of parts of this chapter has appeared in Hoyles, 1988.

11

Pupils' Intuitive Mathematical Conceptions

INTRODUCTION

This chapter is concerned with how the use of Logo within the secondary school mathematics curriculum can allow the teacher to gain insight into pupils' mathematical reality; that is, the way mathematics is learned, how it is perceived and the situational factors embedded within the practices of mathematical activity which affect its subsequent use.

Mathematics educators are becoming aware that pupils do try to make sense of the mathematics presented to them and although the pupil's response is perhaps wrong from the perspective of the teacher it is often rational when viewed in the light of the pupil's past experiences and the setting in which the response took place. As Balacheff suggested, 'Errors are not understood as mere failures of pupils but rather as symptoms of the nature of the conceptions which underlie mathematical activity' (Balacheff, 1984, p. 36). It has also been found that despite exposure to formal methods pupils tend to solve mathematical problems in the informal ways which have worked for them in specific cases (Booth, 1984). In order to help the pupil, the teacher needs therefore to gain insight into pupils' intuitive conceptualisations, to work with these and adapt them to a more formal conceptual framework. The problem for the mathematics teacher is that only the product of the pupil's work is available and the process of solution and way of thinking is not necessarily clear. Talking to pupils elicits information about their conceptualisations but often only an incomplete picture can be obtained since pupils find it difficult to articulate their methods and representations.

It is our contention that Logo programming activity within the mathematics classroom can render pupils' intuitive mathematical conjectures and strategies more accessible to both the pupils themselves and to the teacher. Pupils seem quite naturally to make rough plans and notes during their Logo activity. It is almost as if the 'neat' product on the screen frees them to use pencil and paper for rough work in contrast to their other mathematical activity in which they tend to be 'conditioned' to produce 'neat' work. These rough notes together with diagrams and more systematic methods of recording hands-on interactions indicate the processes of program construction. These processes and the final formalisation in the Logo program then provide a powerful means of illuminating both how the original problem was perceived and how it was solved.

This chapter will discuss some of the insights into pupils' learning of mathematics which have emerged from our analysis of the longitudinal data. It is recognised that some of these intuitions are already known to mathematics educators. The point made here is that the Logo environment makes such pupil conceptions more public, more open to scrutiny by teacher and pupil and more negotiable in ways which are not threatening to pupil self-concept.

THE WAY PUPILS LEARN MATHEMATICS

Fragmented Domains of Knowledge

The longitudinal transcript data has made it possible to trace the development of the knowledge base of the case study pupils over an extended period of time. Observations support the notion that knowledge is fragmented into 'subjective domains of experience' (Bauersfeld, 1984) and that specific concepts must be re-experienced and relearned in different contexts before a synthesis can take place.

An example of this is given by John and Panos's developing understanding of 360 degrees as a total turn over a period of seven months. Before starting the Logo activity Panos and John had successfully completed work from a mathematics booklet which 'covered' 360 degrees being the angle around the point. In their first session they recalled with assistance that there were 360 degrees 'in a circle' and were able to relate this to the drawing of more complete circles in Logo. However, in their next two sessions when attempting to draw a complete circle they consistently adopted an experimental trial-and-error approach and did not use their knowledge of 360 degrees. They produced a rotated pattern of small circles with a turning angle of 22.5 and 50 REPEATs. By counting the image on the screen they worked out that they needed 16 REPEATs when the turning angle was 22.5 but they did not relate these two numbers to 360 degrees. Subsequently, they produced other rotated patterns by using a halving and doubling strategy on the appropriate numbers of an existing complete rotated pattern – that is, 16 REPEATs and a turn of 22.5 was modified to 8 REPEATs and a turn of 45 and so on. John, however, wanted to use a global strategy of 'the smaller the gap the more circles you'd need' to produce the complete rotated patterns.

In order to provoke Panos and John to reflect on these two approaches and discover the relationship between the number of REPEATs and the angle turned in a rotated pattern we grouped them with two girls and gave the four pupils a structured task (Fig. 11.1). Panos initially extended his halving and doubling strategy into the use of proportion: 'I'm thinking how to do it for 18 ... it's not easy ... 24 ... if 6 is 60 ... I think it is 20 ... 60 divided by 3 is ... '

He had decided that, given that 6 REPEATs and a turn of 60 worked, he could multiply and divide by 3 to give 18 REPEATs and a turn of 20 and this method could be extended to numbers other than 3. Underlying Panos's method was an awareness that the product had to be invariant – but this awareness was not explicit at this stage, neither was the size of the invariant.

In order to encourage Panos to recognise explicitly the invariance of the product and develop a global idea of the task rather than rely on his step-by-step 'scaling' strategy, all the group's written records were hidden. (These had listed all the commands for the complete patterns which they had already discovered.) We then invited them to try to find the turning angle for 20 REPEATs. Lucy, who was in the group, suddenly had a flash of insight – delight written all over her face: 'I think it is 28 ... because 20 into 360 is 28.'

Fig. 11.1 The 'Rotated Patterns' Task

FIND THE SECRET OF
THE COMPLETE PATTERN.

Write a procedure to draw a square

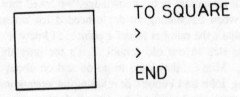

TO SQUARE
>
>
END

Then rotate your square to make a
pattern using the REPEAT command.

How many REPEATS do you need to
make a complete pattern ?

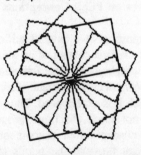

It is a question for debate as to whether the researcher should have
intervened at this point, to provide a calculator for example – so as
to avoid the inevitable disappointment and not to 'lose' Lucy's
suggestion. However, we kept quiet and they typed in REPEAT 20
[HEX RT 28]. Because of the incorrect arithmetic Lucy's conjecture
was shown not to be correct. However, all was not lost and the idea
had now been planted and Panos checked the arithmetic saying:
'360 divided by 20 is 18 not 28.' They now tried this and all the
pupils were delighted with their result. By the end of the session

both Panos and John were able both to use the relationship between the number of REPEATs, the turn and 360 and to articulate it correctly.

In the following session the two boys worked again together as a pair and extended their 'rule' to produce regular polygons. They eventually were able to formalise this and write a generalised regular polygon procedure. Several weeks later they again used the relationship as part of a larger project. We would argue therefore that the fragmented, subjective domains of experience related to turtle turn had at last been synthesised. We discovered, however, when we questioned Panos that he did not perceive that there had been any development in his knowledge. We asked him why he had used 360 when calculating an angle needed for a rotated pattern: 'Because that's the number round a point . . . I knew it . . . they used to teach us that in our old school . . . it's the only thing they did teach us . . . Miss . . . they used to go on and on about it.'

Studying John and Panos's developing understanding of 360 degrees as a total turn has highlighted the lack of spontaneous transfer between 'rote' reproduction of 360 degrees as the 'sum of the angles round a point', an ability to use this in a static context, and understanding in the dynamic context of 360 degrees as a total turn.

Contextual Influences on Pupil Conceptions

From studying the transcripts we have identified many instances in which the context of the first contact of an idea has very obviously influenced its conceptualisation. Discriminations in terms of the characteristics of a new concept are made according to the demands of the context in which it is experienced. Thus sometimes necessary discriminations are not made. In Logo programming 'incorrect' invariants within a concept often become quickly apparent and computer response can provoke the pupils to reflect upon their original abstractions and modify them. None the less, teachers should be alert to the possible problems arising from insufficient variety in past experience. These ideas are illustrated in the following short episodes.

Ray and Helene first used an input of 100 in the REPEAT command in the context of drawing a circle (REPEAT 100 [FD 7 RT 7]). For many sessions they associated this integer input of 100 with the REPEAT command until a project of filling in a square provoked them into trying a different input and finding it worked!

Janet first used the REPEAT command within a procedure in order to draw a rotated hexagon. She persisted for many sessions with the idea that this was the *only* way it could be used. When this misunderstanding became apparent, interventions were made to try to help her to see that the REPEAT command could be used in direct drive. However, tracing through her work suggests that Janet still may not be confident about this. She tends to try out a series of commands in direct drive *without* using the REPEAT command and then collects together appropriate terms with the REPEAT command later in the editor.

A 'classic' case of over-generalisation from a single instance and how the computer interaction can be of assistance is illustrated in the following episode.

In their eighteenth session after considerable experimentation Jude and Linda had discovered that six REPEAT turns of 60 degrees were needed in order to draw a regular hexagon. This discovery led Linda to conjecture, 'Oh, that's excellent ... so what it is is REPEAT 60 for 6 times ... so for an octagon it will probably be REPEAT 80 and for a pentagon REPEAT 50 ... try a pentagon next ... I'm feeling really brainy now ... '

Her generalisation was tested out by typing:

    REPEAT 5 [FD 50 RT 50]

The computer response indicated to Linda that her conjecture was incorrect and provoked her to reflect on the *meaning* of the numbers rather than merely the pattern that they formed.

Pupils Restricting their own Learning Environments

Pupils frequently and spontaneously create a restricted learning environment in their Logo work by using a small domain of numbers as inputs to computer commands. The importance of working in this restricted environment should not be under-estimated in that it provides a framework within which pupils can build up their confidence and feelings of control, yet is flexible enough to allow a considerable amount of creative exploration (see Turkle, 1984). It is, however, important to be aware that the processes by which goals are constructed within these environments may *not* be apparent to the pupils and that the tools available within these environments define what can be done in ways that are not necessarily in the control of the pupils. This is illustrated in the following episode.

183

Throughout the whole of their first year of programming in Logo, Linda and Jude restricted their input to turtle turn to multiples of 45 which were less than or equal to 180. This strategy for angle input influenced the shapes they chose to produce – squares, cubes, rectangular letters – and enabled them to cope easily with parallel lines or symmetrical slanting lines. At the beginning of their second year it was suggested that they draw a regular hexagon in order to provoke them to think about turn and use a wider range of inputs. The pair immediately tried FD 40 RT 45 repeated 6 times and produced an incomplete octagon. This provoked surprise and then experimentation until eventually they came to use a turn of 60 and produced the regular hexagon. When asked why they had always before used multiples of 45 for angle input Linda replied, 'Dunno . . . 'cos we didn't want to explore any different angles, I suppose.'

After they had finished their hexagon they were asked to draw an octagon. They had achieved this *many* times before using their 45-degree strategy. Their actions at this point indicated that they had obviously not reflected on the octagon's construction – that is, the relationship they were applying between the turn and the number of sides. To use 45 degrees was not now their first inclination and they tried to use '6 sides for 60 degrees' so '8 sides for 80 degrees' as described earlier.

PUPILS' CONCEPTIONS OF DECIMALS

We have found many instances of pupils' resistance to the use of their 'formal' knowledge of decimals in the Logo context and inadequacies in their understanding of, for example, the order within decimals. The recent APU survey discusses two types of ordering errors. The first type is called 'decimal point ignored'. In this case, pupils order decimals as if they were whole numbers (so, for example, 0.2 < 0.15). The second type is called 'largest is smallest' in which case the pupils take the number with the most digits after the decimal point to be the smallest number and vice versa, (APU, 1985). Thus pupils consider 0.25 to be smaller than 0.2 because it contains 'more digits after the decimal point'. Brown has explained the nature of pupils' errors with ordering decimals as being a consequence of their thinking 'that the figures after the point represent a "different" number which also has tens, units etc.' (Brown, 1981, p. 51).

Studying pupils' developing use and understanding of decimals was not a major focus of the Logo Maths Project, but as we analysed the data from other perspectives we could not help noticing some difficulties which pupils had with using decimals. We also discovered that certain types of goals needed decimals and provoked pupils to reflect upon the meaning of decimal notation. The 'Scaling Letters' task (Fig. 12.1), for example, turned out to provide a rich context for the exploration of decimals. This section will present several short episodes to illustrate these points.

Resistance to Using Decimals

Janet. Janet felt that decimals were 'peculiar' and was loathe to use them in her Logo work. She had built up an emotional barrier to decimals during previous mathematical experiences (which were not necessarily related to problems in calculation) as illustrated in an interchange with Sally during their fourth Logo session. Sally had calculated that 32.8 was the turning angle needed to draw an eleven-sided regular polygon but Janet wanted to change the goal simply because of the decimal: 'Why don't we do the 12 ... it won't have a point ... '

Later, when drawing a clown's face, the pair wanted to place the nose in the middle of the face which required a move of 'half 15':

Sally   'Now do backwards 7.5.'
Janet   'Forget about .5, it's silly.'

During their second year of using Logo Sally and Janet were given the 'Scaling Letters' task (Fig. 12.1). This task had been primarily designed to provoke the use of variable, but turned out to be valuable in encouraging pupils to use decimals and seeing the effects of decimal inputs to procedures. Janet used decimals in this context for two sessions and we know that this helped her overcome her resistance. Analysis of subsequent transcripts showed that after this experience she accepted decimals, confidently chose to use decimals when appropriate and was able to treat them 'just like other numbers'.

Linda. For the first eighteen months of the project, Linda and Jude's turtle graphics problems did not require them to use decimal input. Whilst working with the 'Scaling Letters' task Linda was encouraged to try decimal inputs. Discussion with her indicated that she was confused about the ordering of decimals *even* in the face of contradictory screen output: 'We done 0.05 and it was pretty small and we done 0.7 and it was even smaller.'

Several weeks later Linda and Jude were asked to draw Fig. 11.2(a). As Linda explained – they planned to draw the 'pine tree' in direct drive and then scale all the distance commands (using the strategy introduced to them in the 'Scaling Letters' task). Linda said, 'We have to do that pattern . . . I thought we might as well do scale and then make it as big or as small as we like.' In direct drive they entered the commands given in Fig. 11.2(b).

Fig. 11.2 Linda and Jude's Solution to the 'Row of Pines' Task

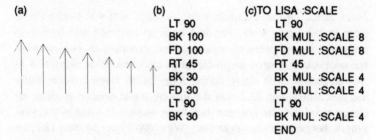

(a)	(b)	(c)TO LISA :SCALE
	LT 90	LT 90
	BK 100	BK MUL :SCALE 8
	FD 100	FD MUL :SCALE 8
	RT 45	RT 45
	BK 30	BK MUL :SCALE 4
	FD 30	FD MUL :SCALE 4
	LT 90	LT 90
	BK 30	BK MUL :SCALE 4
		END

However, their 'multiplication makes bigger' frame and their lack of understanding of decimals meant that they did not attempt to multiply the distances of 100 and 30 by a scaling variable as they had originally planned 'because they would be made too big'. They therefore transformed the distance of 100 to 8 and the distance of 30 to 4 and then multiplied by a scale factor, producing the program given in Fig. 11.2(c). This strategy successfully avoided using any decimal input!

Several weeks later, when Linda was working on a variable sized letter q, we intervened again to persuade Linda to use decimal numbers. Reluctantly she tried 0.2 but then surprisingly became very excited: 'It's so cute . . . let me do the 0.1 . . . I *WANT* to do it.' Linda then spent several sessions developing letter designs using decimals to create very small letters. We believe that for Linda using decimals in this interactive way was a necessary step in her developing understanding of the concept.

Incorrect Ordering of Decimals

Fig. 11.3 Mary and Nadia: 'Variable Star'

(a)   (b)

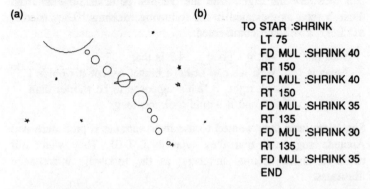

```
TO STAR :SHRINK
    LT 75
    FD MUL :SHRINK 40
    RT 150
    FD MUL :SHRINK 40
    RT 150
    FD MUL :SHRINK 35
    RT 135
    FD MUL :SHRINK 30
    RT 135
    FD MUL :SHRINK 35
    END
```

Mary and Nadia worked on a project of drawing a solar system for 10 sessions over a period of 30 weeks. After drawing all their planets they wanted to design a tiny star (Fig. 11.3a). They tried to design this in direct drive but because their design was so small the screen output was not clear enough for them to check the angles. Mary asked us if they could design a larger star and then 'shrink' it. When they had successfully designed their 'large' star in direct drive they were shown how to write a procedure for their star with a distance scale factor as input (Fig. 11.3b). They then started to 'make sense of' the input to their star procedure. Mary discovered that multiplying distances by 0.5 would make the star smaller. She then predicted that multiplying by 1.5 would also make it smaller because '1.5 is not a whole number'. She typed STAR 1.5 and was of course surprised at the output – an even larger star! She then debugged her ideas about decimals and was able to complete the project by placing small stars of different sizes at different points in the solar system.

Confusion about the Meaning of the Digits in a Decimal

Amanda and Shahidur were working on the 'Scaling Letters' task. They had written a procedure to draw a variable sized letter L. Amanda wanted to try L 8.8 to which Shahidur said: 'You can't have 8.8, 'cos it will be the same size... this way should be smaller...'

187

Shahidur had interpreted the decimal input 8.8 to be a code in which the first 8 effected the size of the vertical part of the L and the second 8 effected the size of the horizontal part of the L. The pair thus saw the digits after the decimal point as separate from those before, as indicated in the following exchange. They tried L 8.7 L 7.5 L 4.2 and commented:

Shahidur   'Ah, it's good . . . 4.2 is that . . . '
Amanda   'Well we can make it bigger except it wouldn't look right . . . that's supposed to be shorter than that and it would look too long.'

Sometime later they wanted to use their variable L procedure and Amanda suggested that they type in L 0.01. They were still confused about decimal numbers, as the following interchange illustrates.

Shahidur   'It's the other way round.'
Amanda   'No, it was 0.01 but that only made a line this way and it didn't make a line this way, did it?'

They tried L 0.01 which produced a small dot. They could not understand what had happened, so we tried to explain that there was a vertical and horizontal part of L being drawn but that the image was so small that the vertical component could not be seen. Shahidur's continuing misconception of decimals is evident in his response.

Shahidur   'Yeah Miss, but it can't go that way because, you know, we haven't done a number for this way . . . we just done a number for this way.' (meaning we've only done a number for the horizontal part)

At the beginning of the next session the pair decided to make a pattern with their general letter procedures. Amanda wanted to try out L 1.5 but Shahidur predicted that this would not draw an L. He still thought that the '1' of the 1.5 would effect the vertical part of the L and the '5' of the 1.5 would effect the horizontal part of the L. They tried L 1.5 at this point, the light began to dawn and Shahidur started to 'make sense of' the computer response.

Shahidur   'Miss, you know 1.5 . . . is it 60 that way and that way?'

He was beginning to understand that the 1.5 multiplied the 40 in both the vertical and horizontal components of the L. The screen response to L 1.5 contributed to this understanding.

When Amanda and Shahidur started to use decimal input they could not conceive of a decimal as a 'whole', but thought about it as made up of separate parts which acted on the separate parts of the geometrical object being constructed. The computer response was crucial in helping them to come to an understanding of a decimal number as a 'whole' and as this understanding developed they were able to reflect on the effect of this 'whole' on the distance commands within their 'scaled' procedure.

PUPILS' CONCEPTIONS OF RATIO AND PROPORTION

Proportional reasoning has been the object of a great many studies. Several of these studies have examined the different strategies employed in solving proportions and identified variations in successful strategies and common unsuccessful strategies. The Concepts in Secondary Mathematics and Science project (CSMS), for example, analysed the difficulties children have with the idea of ratio and used these to formulate levels of understanding (Hart, 1981). This work found evidence for the following 'hypothesis' as reported in Hart (1984): '1. The incorrect answers given to certain questions on the CSMS tests all arose from the use of an identifiable incorrect reasoning pattern, referred to as "the incorrect addition strategy". 2. The children using "the incorrect addition strategy" have evolved their own methods of solving easy ratio questions, these methods being non-multiplicative. 3. These children viewed ratio, proportion and certainly enlargement as requiring the operation of addition and not multiplication' (Hart, 1984, p. 8).

In a useful review of the literature in this area, Tourniaire and Pulos (1985) point out that 'the research has become increasingly sophisticated, changing from a view of proportional reasoning as a global ability, or a manifestation of a general cognitive structure, to a more differentiated view focusing on describing the procedures used in proportional reasoning and how they are influenced by task and person parameters' (p. 181). We are then led to enquire why multiplication seems to be so much more difficult to see in a situation than addition. Hoyles and Noss (1989) suggest that 'a likely reason is that children's intuitive knowledge about multiplication is much weaker, their world is multiplication-impoverished (witness the difficulty we have in thinking about images of multiplication for the classroom compared with addition). Contexts requiring multiplication (by numbers other than say 2 or 10) – much less proportion – are not an everyday part of most children's experience' (p. 55).

We therefore need to explore different task settings and how they might provoke pupils to adopt different strategies. Although the project did not set out to investigate pupils' conceptions of ratio and proportion, pupils did bump up against these ideas and we report some of the relevant data here.

Sally and Janet had completed the ARROW task as described in Chapter 9. The task they had been given was as in Fig. 11.4 below.

Fig. 11.4 The 'Arrow' Task

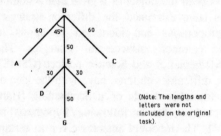

(Note: The lengths and letters were not included on the original task).

MAKE A PROCEDURE TO DRAW THIS SHAPE AS BIG OR AS SMALL AS YOU WISH.

The pair had, however, ignored the difference in size of AB and BE. An intervention was made at this point to nudge them to reflect on any differences between the given figure and the screen image.

Intervention 'Are you sure that's exactly the same as that?'

Sally answered confidently that the two images were the same so it was suggested that they measure all the lengths to check. They then realised the discrepancy and were willing to try again. Janet immediately suggested that they add another input for the new length BE.

Janet   'Yeh, so what we have to do is we have to make, say, JILL now.'

She then explained how she wanted to substitute JILL for all the 'bits' of the central stem of the ARROW.

Janet	'... so it's this one and this one and we have to change ... so it's those two and those two we've got to change to JILL!'

The pair agreed to this 'adding on' strategy for inputs – that is, every part of a figure which is perceived to vary is given a new input without explicit recognition of any internal relationship between the inputs. They typed:

HILL :JILL :JACK

This formulation made Sally stop to reflect. She realised that *any* two numbers as inputs would not work!

Sally	'You can put any number in but it won't be the same ...'

At first Sally suggested subtraction as the relationship between JACK and JILL, and Janet agreed – but at the point of writing this in Logo, that is as Janet proposed, FD SUB :JACK 10, Sally again stopped to reflect.

Sally	'Wait, if it gets bigger would it still be 10?'

This is a critical observation. Sally seemed to be 'seeing the general in the specific' and recognising that the operation of subtraction would not work. Janet did not understand her point:

Janet	'... it would be right because you've got your hundred, OK? ... and you're subtracting 10 and you've got 90 ... you'll always be subtracting 10 'cos it's 10 less, isn't it?'

This comment provoked Sally to try to explain her reservations and develop her argument more precisely in the face of continued opposition:

Sally	'... but if it's double as big then they would be double as small.'
Janet	'What?'
Sally	'Right, if this was 12 and it was subtract 10 then we'd only need 11 ... it wouldn't be the same.'
Janet	'It would.'
Sally	'It wouldn't, 'cos ... say we subtract 1 from 6 would be 5 but then this would be 10 next time.'
Janet	'I dunno, I dunno what you're talking about ...'

Finally, Sally was able to fully articulate her argument:

Sally 'Look, this is 5 and if we made it twice as big
     that's 10 . . . and this is 6 and if this was twice as
     big it would be 12 . . . yeh? . . . and if you said
     SUB JACK 10 that would give you 11 and that's
     too long for that.'

At this stage Sally did not know what operation to propose but she
was convinced that an additive strategy would *not* work. **The fact
that the inputs were declared on the turtle line of the Logo
program and Sally knew that they could represent a whole
range of numbers seemed to be important in this context.** Janet,
however, took over at this point and used subtraction since no other
alternative was forthcoming.

At the end of the session the issue came up again as a result of
the visual feedback, which indicated that subtraction had *not* been
the correct operation. Sally now knew that the operation required
was multiplication but could not work out the number to use to
multiply.

Sally 'There must be a number that you can do
     something with . . . there must be some way to
     get the length of that the same as that . . . I don't
     know. That's what we've got to find out.'

On this particular occasion it proved too hard for the pair to work
out the exact relationship required *but* the activity showed the *need*
for a multiplicative relationship and the rejection of an additive
strategy.

IMPLICATIONS FOR CLASSROOM PRACTICE

We have in this chapter attempted to draw together our insights into
pupils' mathematical thinking gained through observation of their
Logo work. We have observed the fragmented way that knowledge
is developed and how it is inextricably interrelated with unexpected
features drawn from the setting in which it was first experienced.
We are now far clearer about emotional influences on pupil
programming – how pupils often restrict their problem-solving
activity to build up confidence with the computer and as a result
are not necessarily aware of the processes by which their projects
came to be constructed; how pupils frequently refuse to use

mathematical notions in Logo which they have learnt to fear during previous mathematics learning. We have described how Logo programming has highlighted pupil misconceptions (of decimals for example) but has also provided a bridge to understanding – through cognitive conflict provoked by the computer feedback, through experimentation leading to acceptance of the idea and finally through providing a dynamic representation of mathematics which pushes pupils into seeing the general in the specific (in relation to ratio and proportion for example). We suggest that the episodes we describe will increase teachers' awareness of the pupil perspective. Thus teachers will be better able to decide the activities necessary to help the pupils move from intuitive to more formal mathematical frameworks in both Logo and non-Logo contexts.

12

Understanding Algebraic Ideas

INTRODUCTION

Algebra as a mathematical language has developed over the centuries from its first introduction as a tool to solve equations in which a letter or symbol represented a particular but unknown number (at the time of Diophantus, circa 250 AD) to classical generalised arithmetic in which symbols were used to represent relationships between variables (at the time of Vieta in the early seventeenth century) to finally the more general study of structures known as modern algebra. Modern algebra can be thought of as a language which enables the similarities in structure between different mathematical systems to be made explicit. Algebra has played a central role in school mathematics for many years and although more recently the teaching of algebra has been given less emphasis, Byers and Erlwanger stress that 'We can no more dispense with teaching algebraic symbolism than teaching place-value notation. Symbolic expressions are transformed more easily than their verbal counterparts so that they not only save time and labour but they also aid the understanding of content' (Byers and Erlwanger, 1984, p. 265).

Research into children's understanding of algebra has highlighted the problems children have with interpreting the meaning of letters and with formalising and symbolising a generalisable method (Küchemann, 1981; Booth, 1984). Booth suggests that 'If children do not have the structure available in the arithmetic case, they are unlikely to produce it (or understand it) in the algebra case' (Booth, 1984, p. 102). As Harper points out, 'The step between the Diophantine and the Vietan system took place over a period of more than 1300 years. In the classroom this step must often be taken over a period of less than five years; the present indications are that few pupils actually achieve it' (Harper, 1987, p. 86).

First and foremost, mathematics educators need to find problems which provoke the use of algebra and in which algebra is meaningful and not simply a set of manipulations. This is not an easy task in 'traditional' school mathematics. However, we suggest that the computer programming context does provide problem situations in which variable *is* a meaningful problem-solving tool. It seems appropriate, therefore, to consider the ways in which the computer can enhance the learning of algebra. In an exploratory study with eight pupils (aged 10+) who had learned Logo for eighteen months, Noss (1986) reported that 'Children may under the appropriate conditions make use of the algebra they have used in a Logo environment, in order to construct algebraic meaning in a non-computational context' (Noss, 1986, p. 354). However, research also suggests that the use of variable is not likely to occur 'naturally' and that 'aside from difficulties in defining a general procedure there is more basically a lack of an immediate sense of the necessity to define such procedures' (Hillel and Samurçay, 1985, p. 8).

This chapter investigates the notion that certain programming experiences in Logo will provide pupils with a conceptual basis for variable which will enhance their work with 'paper and pencil' algebra. The materials which were used to help pupils link the conception of variable derived within a Logo context to a non-Logo context are described and evaluated. In addition, pupils' understanding of algebra-related ideas in a 'paper and pencil' context is interpreted in the light of their use and understanding of variable in Logo.

THE CONCEPT OF VARIABLE IN LOGO

Since variables are used in different ways depending on the particular programming environment, it is useful to set out how variables operate in Logo. First, variables can be defined either as global or local. A global variable is assigned at top level (that is, not within any procedure) by means of the MAKE statement. It can then be used within all procedures and subprocedures and only ceases to exist when the computer is switched off. A local variable, in contrast, is part of procedure definition and exists only within the procedure and any subprocedures called by it. A local variable is a parameter through which a value is passed to a procedure. The following is an example:

```
TO SQUARE :SIDE
    REPEAT 4 [FD :SIDE RT 90]
    END
```

The variable SIDE is named in the title line of the procedure and then used within the procedure; thus the variable SIDE is used as a means by which a value is passed to the procedure SQUARE. The value of SIDE is assigned when the procedure SQUARE is invoked. Typing SQUARE 30 will cause the computer to execute the procedure SQUARE by assigning the value 30 to the variable called SIDE. The variable SIDE ceases to exist within the computer memory when the procedure SQUARE has been processed.

Local variables are the means by which values are passed from procedures to subprocedures. They thus have a close relationship to issues of subprocedure, modularity and sequencing as well as to ideas of output and recursion. In the Logo Maths Project, we tried to develop a consistent approach to the teaching and learning of Logo as a programming language which took advantage of its modular nature. We decided therefore to introduce pupils predominantly to local variables and not to global variables. In fact there was only one occasion when pupils used a global variable throughout the three years of the Project. This meant that the pupils did not (apart from this one occasion) use variable in the assignment statement MAKE. Finally, it should be noted that we were concerned with pupils' use and understanding of algebra-related ideas in a Logo environment as part of school mathematics. We were not therefore concerned with the pupils' understanding of variable from a computer science perspective.

The concept of variable in Logo was studied from the perspective of a 'conceptual field' (Vergnaud, 1982). The idea of a conceptual field is useful as it puts bounds on the concept under study but also allows for the inevitable overlap between concepts. Central to the idea of a conceptual field is the crucially important interrelationship between the set of problem situations which use the concept, the set of invariants which constitute the concept and the symbolic systems used to represent the concept.

As far as problem situations are concerned within a turtle geometry domain a general procedure produces a 'varying' effect on the screen. It is therefore reasonable to hypothesise that defining and working with general turtle geometry procedures would be a sound introduction to variable in a visual dimension and would be easier for pupils than defining non-turtle geometry procedures. A general procedure can either arise out of a solution to a well-defined problem or it can arise out of a loosely-defined activity in which the subprocedure is built up through interaction with the computer (see Chapter 4 for a more detailed discussion of this). It is therefore likely that the dimension well-defined/loosely-defined will effect the cognitive demands of any task.

Analysis of the first eighteen months of transcript data from the Logo Maths Project indicated however that, first, pupils rarely chose projects which 'needed' the concept of variable and, second, that even when the researcher perceived a need for variable in a pupil's project or in a 'teacher-given' task, and intervened appropriately, there was resistance to the use of the idea. This was the case for both pupils with little and pupils with no experience of variable in 'paper and pencil' algebra. (It should be noted that the pupils were following their 'normal' mathematics curriculum and the type and amount of algebra work carried out by the pupils was therefore known by, but not in the control of, the research team.) It was very apparent that pupils found it difficult to conceive of a project which needed the idea of variable. They had not had sufficient experience to appreciate the potential of variable. It was decided therefore to introduce the concept of variable to all the pupils within a series of structured tasks. The first such task, the 'Scaling Letter' task (Fig. 12.1) aimed to provoke the pupils to use variable as a tool to solve problems and then later to develop the idea of variable as an object for manipulation.

After defining the letter L the pupils were shown how to change their fixed L procedure to a general L procedure according to written instructions. They were asked to try a range of inputs to the L procedure. The suggested inputs on the sheet were specifically chosen so as to include decimal and negative numbers. In the context of defining the biggest and smallest letter on the screen the pupils found that they had to use decimal inputs to their L procedure. Although this task had been chosen as an introduction to variable, it should also be noted that it provided the motivation for using decimal input – important in itself in the developing understanding of variable as representing a range of numbers. (This is discussed in more detail in Chapter 11.)

Fig. 12.1 The 'Scaling Letter' Task

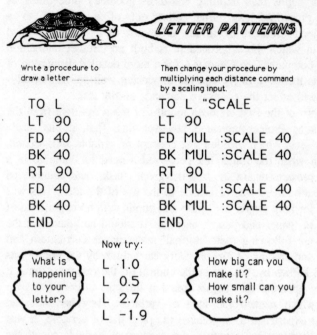

Write a procedure to draw a letter ....

```
TO L
LT 90
FD 40
BK 40
RT 90
FD 40
BK 40
END
```

Then change your procedure by multiplying each distance command by a scaling input.

```
TO L "SCALE
LT 90
FD MUL :SCALE 40
BK MUL :SCALE 40
RT 90
FD MUL :SCALE 40
BK MUL :SCALE 40
END
```

Now try:

What is happening to your letter?

```
L 1.0
L 0.5
L 2.7
L -1.9
```

How big can you make it?
How small can you make it?

When a pupil pair had confidently used a range of inputs to the L procedure they were asked to define any other variable letter of their choice and to build up a design on the screen. This building-up process frequently pushed the pupils into using variable input to a general superprocedure which called a general subprocedure (see, for example, Figs 12.2 and 12.3).

Fig. 12.2 Sally and Janet: Extension of the 'Scaling Letter' Task

```
TO LONG :SCALE
STEP
L :SCALE
MOVE :SCALE
O :SCALE
MOVE :SCALE
N :SCALE
MOVE :SCALE
G :SCALE
END
```

```
TO N :SCALE
LT 90
FD MUL :SCALE 40
LT 45
BK MUL :SCALE 57
RT 45
FD MUL :SCALE 40
BK MUL :SCALE 40
LIFT
RT 90
BK MUL :SCALE 40
PD
END
```

```
TO STEP
   LIFT
   BK 150
   PD
END
```

```
TO MOVE :SCALE
   LIFT
   FD MUL :SCALE 50
   PD
END
```

```
TO L :SCALE
   LT 90
   FD MUL :SCALE 40
   BK MUL :SCALE 40
   RT 90
   FD MUL :SCALE 40
   BK MUL :SCALE 40
END
```

```
TO O :SCALE
   FD MUL :SCALE 40
   RT 90
   BK MUL :SCALE 40
   RT 90
   FD MUL :SCALE 40
   RT 90
   BK MUL :SCALE 40
   RT 90
END
```

```
TO G :SCALE
   RT 90
   BK MUL :SCALE 40
   RT 90
   BK MUL :SCALE 40
   FD MUL :SCALE 40
   RT 90
   FD MUL :SCALE 40
   RT 90
   BK MUL :SCALE 20
   RT 90
   FD MUL :SCALE 20
   PU
   FD MUL :SCALE 20
   RT 90
   BK MUL :SCALE 20
   RT 90
   PD
END
```

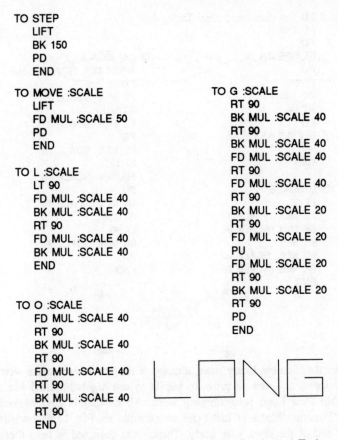

Fig. 12.3 Linda and Elaine: Extension of 'Scaling Letter' Task

```
TO PARTYTIME
   EL2 2 2
   PU
   RT 180
   FD 120
   RT 90
   FD 70
   RT 90
   PD
   EL2 0.5 0.5
   PU
   RT90
   FD120
   LT90
   PD
   EL2 0.5 0.5
```

```
TO EL2 :JIM :TIM
   QE2 :JIM
   LE2 :TIM
END
```

```
TO QE2 :JIM
   REPEAT 8 [QU :JIM LT 45]
END
```

```
TO LE2 :TIM
   REPEAT 8 [L :TIM LT 45]
END
```

```
PU
FD 230
PD
EL2 0.5 0.5                  TO  QU :SCALE
PU                              ARCR MUL :SCALE 7 360
LT 90                           PU
FD 130                          FD MUL :SCALE 3
RT 90                           RT 90
PD                              FD MUL :SCALE 3
EL2 0.5 0.5                     PD
HT                              FD MUL :SCALE 30
END                             LT 135
                                FD MUL :SCALE 10
TO  L 'SCALE                    PU
LT 90                           BK MUL :SCALE 10
FD MUL :SCALE 40                RT 135
BK MUL :SCALE 40                LT 90
RT 90                           BK MUL :SCALE 7
FD MUL :SCALE 20                PD
BK MUL :SCALE 20                END
END
```

After the 'Scaling Letter' task, a range of teacher-devised tasks were developed in order to provoke pupils to use algebra-related ideas within their Logo programming work. All the pupils also worked on 'Function Machine' tasks (for an example see Fig. 12.9) towards the end of the three-year study. These were designed to help them make links between variable in Logo and variable in 'paper and pencil' algebra and are discussed more fully later in this chapter.

We will now present our analysis of the meaning of variable in Logo programming from the perspective of the pupil. By carrying out an ongoing analysis of the situations in which pupils used variable to define general procedures, the following categories of variable use were identified. These categories provide a framework from which to analyse the pupils' understanding of algebra-related ideas in Logo.

(I) One variable input to a procedure
(S) Variable input as scale factor
(N) More than one variable input to a procedure
(O) Variable input operated on within a procedure
(F) Variable input to define a mathematical function in Logo

(G) General superprocedure
(R) Recursive procedure

The following is a description of these categories.

(I) One variable input to a procedure. Situations in which the variable has not been operated on within the procedure are included in this category (Fig. 12.4). This variable could represent: (a) a positive integer in, for example, the number of 'REPEATs'; (b) a real number in, for example, a distance or angle command. When pupils use one variable input they are using variable as a place-holder for a set of numbers and it was anticipated that this would assist the understanding of variable as a general unknown in algebra.

Fig. 12.4 Procedure with One Variable Input

```
TO TRIANGLE :SIDE
    REPEAT 3 [FD :SIDE RT 90]
    END
```

(S) Variable input as scale factor. This category concerns situations in which a variable input is used to scale all the distance commands in a turtle graphics procedure. This type of variable input can be used by pupils as a way of generalising a fixed procedure (Fig. 12.5a) without making explicit the geometrical relationships within the procedure. Initially it was expected that the idea of changing a fixed procedure to a general procedure by scaling distance commands would be conceptually easier for pupils to use than making a general relationship explicit by operating on a variable input within a procedure (category (O) below). When pupils use input as a scaling factor they can define a general procedure from a fixed procedure without necessarily having reflected upon the invariants within their procedure.

(N) More than one variable input to a procedure. This category includes situations in which pupils use more than one variable input to their procedure (Fig. 12.5b). Variable inputs are added to a general procedure for each 'object' which varies and thus any relationship between variables is not made explicit (Hoyles, 1987). We suggest that using more than one input in this way is conceptually easier than operating on a variable within a procedure.

(O) Variable input operated on within a procedure. This category includes situations in which any general relationship between variables within a procedure is made explicit by operating on one or more variable inputs within the procedure (Fig. 12.5c). In order

to do this pupils need to identify what is variable and what is invariant and need to be able to formalise the necessary relationships.

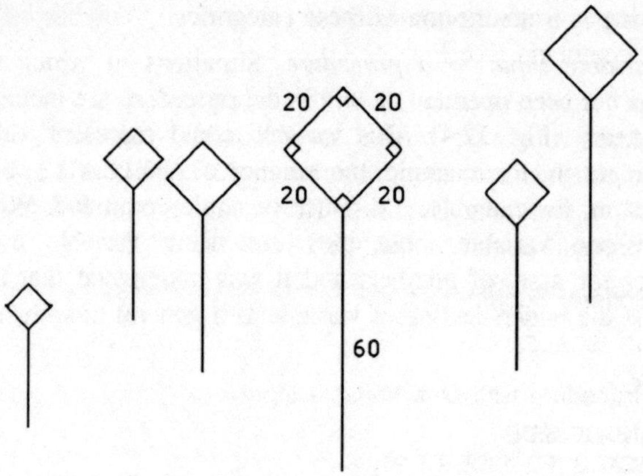

I want a procedure which will draw
this shape but I want to make it as
big or as small as I like. Can you write
me a procedure to do this?

(a)	(b)	(c)
TO TOM :SCALE	TO KITE :YT :HT	TO SQUAN :NUM
LT 90	RT 45	LT 135
PU	FD :YT	REPEAT 4 [FD
BK 90	RT 90	:NUM RT 90]
PD	FD :YT	LT 135
FD MUL :SCALE 60	RT 90	FD MUL :NUM 3
LT 45	FD :YT	END
FD MUL :SCALE 20	RT 90	
RT 90	FD :YT	
FD MUL :SCALE 20	BD :YT	
RT 90	RT 90	
FD MUL :SCALE 20	FD :YT	
RT 90	RT 45	
FD MUL :SCALE 20	FD :HT	
END	END	

Fig. 12.5 (a) Variable as Scale Factor; **(b)** More than One Variable Input; **(c)** Variable Operated On

(F) Variable input to define a mathematical function in Logo. In this category a procedure acts like a mathematical function. A variable is input and then is operated on within the procedure and the result output from the procedure to be used by another Logo function or command (see Fig. 12.8a).

(G) General superprocedure. This category refers to general superprocedures which use general subprocedures (Fig. 12.6). It is important to consider the use of variable in the context of Logo as a structured programming language. This means that nested layers of general procedures can be defined.

Fig. 12.6 General Superprocedure

```
TO LONG :SCALE
    STEP
    L :SCALE
    MOVE :SCALE
    O :SCALE
    MOVE :SCALE
    N :SCALE
    MOVE :SCALE
END
```

(R) Recursive procedure. This category refers to general recursive procedures. In the Logo Maths Project pupils only used tail recursive procedures (Fig. 12.7).

Fig. 12.7 Tail Recursive Procedure

```
TO CORRIDOR :DISTANCE
    FD :DISTANCE
    RT 90
    CORRIDOR ADD :DISTANCE 1
END
```

LINKING LOGO AND ALGEBRA THROUGH FUNCTIONS

Logo is a functional programming language, the underlying model of which is isomorphic to the idea of mathematical function. It is possible to define and build up functions, composite functions and inverse functions in Logo which model the behaviour of functions in mathematics. The following example based on an elementary mathematical function will serve to illustrate this point. Figures 12.8b and c give two common forms of representation of a simple function, while Fig. 12.8a gives its equivalent representation in Logo:

Fig. 12.8 Function Representations

(a) TO F :X	(b) IN	OUT	(c) F(X) = X + 4
OUTPUT ADD :X 4	3	→ 7	
END	–2	→ 2	or X → X + 4
	1.5	→ 5.5	

All the representations in Fig. 12.8 can be thought of as different representations of the same function. Associated with any function is a domain and this can be defined for both the mathematical and the Logo function. Associated with each member of the domain is a unique value. In order to define a function in Logo it is necessary to use the idea of output – the means by which this value is passed out from the procedure.

In both the algebra and the Logo representation changing the name of the variable does not change the function itself. So, for example, H(y) = y - 7 is the same function as H(w) = w - 7 and in Logo:

```
TO H :y          is the same as     TO H :w
   OUTPUT SUB :y 7                      OUTPUT SUB :w 7
   END                                  END
```

A composite function can also be represented in Logo in a way which matches the algebraic representation.

This chapter is concerned with pupils' understanding of variable and not with their understanding of function. Nevertheless it was decided to base materials designed to help pupils make links between variable in Logo and variable in algebra on the idea of function because of the similarity in structures within the two contexts. All the pupils had experienced about 50 hours of turtle graphics computer programming before working on the function machine tasks. The primary aim of these tasks was to serve as a bridge between function in Logo and function in algebra. Subsidiary aims were:

- to extend pupils' use of variable to a non-graphics context in which a variable represents a number;
- to move pupils from using words for variable names to single letters (which are normally encountered in the algebra situation);
- to extend pupils' experience of using 'unclosed' variable expressions in Logo;
- to provoke pupils to use decimal and negative numbers and in doing so extend their understanding of a variable as representing a range of numbers;

- to confront pupils with the idea that changing the symbol within a function does not imply changing the referent of the symbol.

The pupils' function machine experience consisted of two activities: a computer-based activity and a 'paper-and-pencil'-based activity.

Computer-based Activity

Fig. 12.9 The 'Function Machine' Task

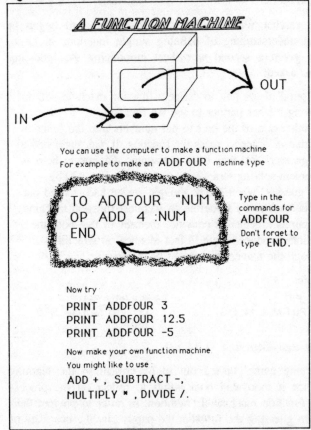

Working in their pairs pupils were given a worksheet (Fig. 12.9) asking them to define a simple arithmetic function. This was the first time that any of the case study pupils had used the Logo idea of output. The worksheet directed the pupils to try different inputs to the 'function' machine. They were asked to experiment with a range of inputs. The inputs were specifically chosen to include a decimal number and a negative number in order to extend the pupils' notion of 'any number'. The teacher also asked the pupils to use a range of variable names including single-letter names. The following are examples of some of the procedures which were defined:

```
TO LL :L                    TO HAZEL :NUT
   OUTPUT MUL 1.5 :L            OUTPUT DIV :NUT 3
   END                         END
   (equivalent to x → 1.5x)    (equivalent to y → y/3)
```

When the teacher felt confident that the pupils had begun to develop an understanding of defining simple functions in Logo, they were given a second worksheet introducing the 'guessing game'. This asked:

1. One pupil of the pair to define a function machine without allowing his/her partner to see the function.
2. The other one of the pair to put numbers into the function machine in order to guess the function. It was suggested to the 'guesser' that they draw a mapping diagram to help as a problem-solving tool (see, for example, Fig. 12.8b).
3. The 'guesser' when she/he thought she/he had worked out the function to try to define an identical function machine.
4. The pupils together to convince themselves that both the functions produced were in fact identical in structure – although the names used might be different.

For example:

```
TO MAT :PIG                 TO MULRED :RED
   OUTPUT MUL 14 :PIG          OUTPUT MUL 14 :RED
   END                        END
```

are both equivalent to $z → 14 z$.

This 'guessing game' turned out to be critical in the learning process since it motivated both pupils to reflect on the process within the function machine. In addition, in order to prevent their partner from guessing the function the pupils saw the necessity of choosing function names which were not linked to the effect of the machine.

Paper and Pencil Activity

Approximately one month after the pupils had tried out the 'hands-on' function material the pupils worked away from the computer on a series of paper and pencil tasks. All the pupils were handed the same starting worksheet and then proceeded to work at their own pace. All the pupils in fact completed the material within a one-hour session. The task was of the following form:

1. Worksheets (see, for example, Fig. 12.10) directing pupils to write down Logo functions equivalent to a range of mapping diagrams. The aim was to consolidate the link between the mapping diagram and the Logo representation.
2. A worksheet giving the pupils the 'conversions' between Logo and algebra notation and directing pupils to make some further conversions for themselves.
3. Worksheets directing pupils to write down both the Logo and the algebra representation of some given mapping diagrams.

When the pupils had completed these tasks they were asked to write down the algebra representations of all the functions which they had constructed and used from a Logo perspective. Comparisons between the pupils' final algebra representations and their original Logo representations were then used as a basis for analysing whether or not the pupils had made links between the two representations.

Pupils were allowed to freely discuss amongst themselves the nature of a function represented by the mapping diagram. In spite of this prior discussion, it is noteworthy that pupils used different notations to represent the same function.

The Importance of the Function Work

When defining a function in Logo the syntax of the representation is critical. Although initially some of the pupils found the specific nature of the Logo syntax difficult to remember this was only a brief phase given the practical nature of the Logo work, and by the end of the sessions all the pupils were able to define simple functions whilst working at the computer. The 'guessing' game was important in engaging both of the pupils in a pair in the 'hands-on' activity of defining functions. We also noticed that before

Fig. 12.10 The 'Paper and Pencil Function Machine' Task

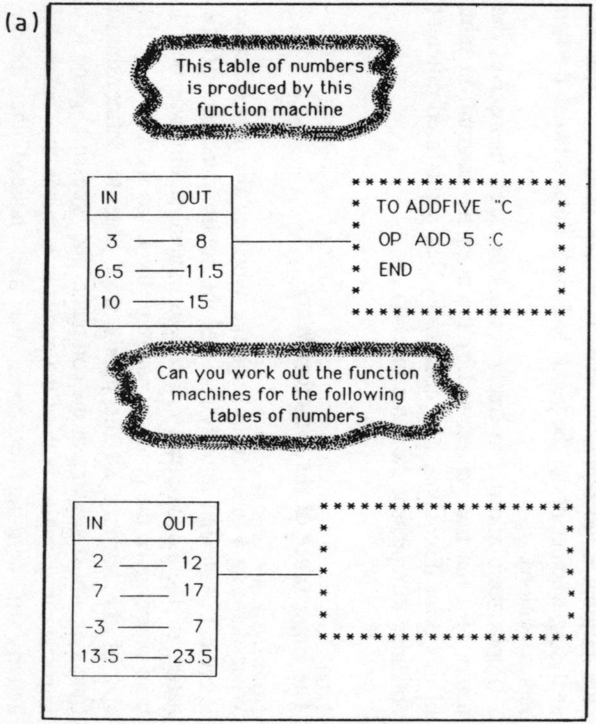

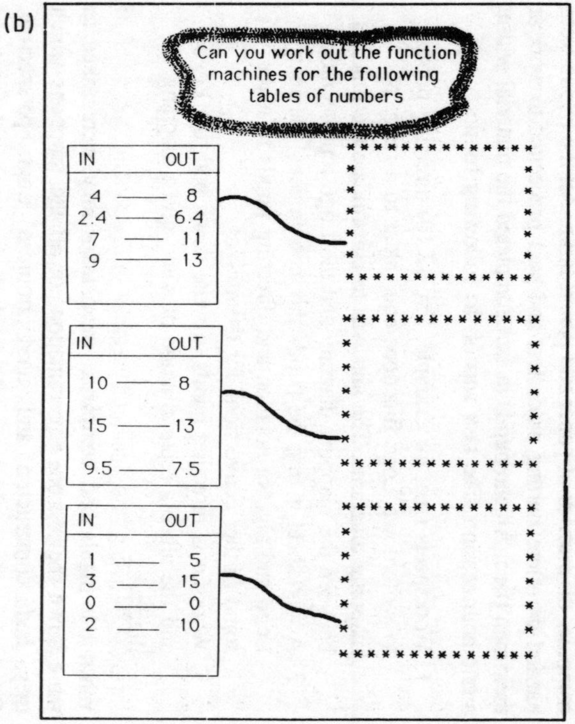

participating in this game the pupils tended not to reflect on the relationship of the input to the output in a defined function. Thus the rules of the game provided the incentive for the pupils to reflect on the process within their defined functions. In addition, writing a mapping diagram down on paper proved important in provoking pupils to reflect on the processes involved in defining a simple function. The fact that pupils were free to choose any variable name and any function name also appears to have been important from the point of view of motivation – pupils enjoyed creating the names. Finally, in playing the game it was possible for pupils with their partners to find their own level of working; for example, some pupils rapidly defined functions for all the arithmetic operations while others spent longer making sense of addition functions only. Although the pupils almost always used positive whole numbers as inputs to their function machines the resultant outputs frequently included decimal and negative numbers and thus provoked a new awareness of these numbers.

The paper and pencil function tasks provided an important 'bridge' between the idea of variable in Logo and the idea of variable in algebra. There was a very obvious relationship between the Logo representation of a function constructed by the majority of case study pupils and its algebraic representation. For example, Linda had written down the following Logo representation for a 'multiply by 5' function:

```
TO MULFIVE :M
    OUTPUT MUL :M 5
    END
```

At a later stage during the task when asked to write down the algebra representation for the same function, she wrote down:

$$M \rightarrow M5.$$

Linda had never come across algebra as part of her 'normal' mathematics lesson and her algebra representation was a direct translation from the Logo representation.

PUPILS' UNDERSTANDING OF VARIABLE

In order to analyse the longitudinal case study pupils' understanding of variable the following categories were devised:

- Acceptance of the 'idea of variable';
- Understanding that any variable name can be used;
- Understanding that a variable name represents a range of numbers;
- Understanding that different variable names can represent the same value;
- Acceptance of 'lack of closure' in a variable-dependent expression;
- Ability to establish a second-order relationship between variable-dependent expressions;
- Ability to use variable to formalise a general method.

All the pupils were given an individual structured interview at the end of the three-year project. In addition pupils visited the university laboratories to carry out, individually, tasks devised to probe their understanding of variable in Logo.

Individual tasks. At the end of the project all the case study pupils spent a day working individually on specific Logo tasks. These tasks were the 'Variable Squares' task, the 'Lollipop' task (Fig. 7.3), and the 'Decreasing Squares' task (Fig. 10.3). Not surprisingly it was found that the pupils' 'hands-on' experience of using variable in Logo directly affected their solutions to these tasks (see Table 12.1). Shahidur and Ravi solved all three tasks by using variable as a scale factor which had been their predominant experience of variable use. Linda either used variable as a scale factor or, as in the case of the Lollipop task, defined two separate procedures, one for the 'stick' and one for the 'sweet', both having one input. She did not attempt, on her own, to combine these procedures into a superprocedure. Sally, Janet, Asim and George did not use variable as a scale factor as a means of solving any of these tasks. Only George, Asim and Jude solved the task by operating on a variable. Evidence from the transcript data indicates that pupils will either ignore a given ratio or 'simplify' it to one of 'halving and doubling' unless specifically told not to do so. This indicates that more attention needs to be paid to devising tasks in which it is necessary to operate on a variable in order to solve the task. We suggest that it is only when pupils are able to use variable in the category 'Variable operated on' that they have made the break from arithmetical to algebraic thought within the Logo context.

Individual interviews. In order to probe the case study pupils' understanding of algebra-related ideas in both Logo and paper and pencil algebra, they were all given a structured interview which included paper and pencil tasks. Within the interview they were asked to:

- Make a generalisation and formalise it in an algebra context.
- Make a generalisation and formalise it in a Logo context.
- Answer algebra questions related to the meaning of letters taken from the Concepts in Secondary Mathematics and Science project (see also, for example, Figs 12.11 and 12.12a).
- Answer Logo questions related to the meaning of variable names (see, for example, Fig. 12.12b).
- Represent a function in both Logo and algebra.

A similar group of pupils to the case study pupils were interviewed in order to provide another perspective from which to analyse the case study pupils' responses to the algebra-related questions of the structured interview. This group of pupils was called the comparison group.

This section will discuss the results of the interviews both from the point of view of the case study pupils' understanding of variable in Logo and from the point of view of their understanding in paper and pencil algebra. Table 12.2 presents an overview of the results of the structured interviews for both the longitudinal case study and the comparison pupils.

Acceptance of the idea of variable. All the case study pupils attempted the interview questions and therefore accepted the idea of variable within the paper and pencil algebra and Logo questions. Four of the eight case study pupils had never done any algebra within their 'normal' mathematics lessons and we suggest that the Logo experience of variable provided these pupils with a framework from which understanding could develop.

Understanding that any variable name can be used. Before pupils can use and manipulate a variable they have to name it. When pupils are first introduced to variable they frequently attach too much significance to the variable name. On the one hand, choosing a meaningful name helps pupils to accept the object but, on the other hand, the meaningful name may lure pupils into thinking that the name itself has some meaning and some power. We suggest that pupils need to be encouraged to use a range of variable names,

Table 12.1 Case Study Pupils' Solutions to Individual Logo Programming Tasks by Reference to Variable Use

	Variable Squares Task	Decreasing Squares Task	Lollipop Task
Sally	(I) One variable input	(G) General superprocedure (O) Variable operated on	(N) More than one variable input
Asim	(I) One variable input	(I) One variable input	(O) Variable operated on
George	(I) One variable input	(I) General superprocedure (O) Variable operated on	(O) Variable operated on
Janet	(I) One variable input	(I) One variable input (for subprocedure)	(N) More than one variable input (unrelated)
Jude	(I) One variable input	(I) One variable input (for subprocedure)	(O) Variable operated on
Ravi	(S) Variable as scale factor	No input used	(S) Variable as scale factor
Linda	(I) One variable input	(I) One variable input (for subprocedure)	(N) More than one variable input (unrelated)
Shahidur	(S) Variable as scale factor	(S) Variable as scale factor	(S) Variable as scale factor

including 'nonsense' names (which they know have no meaning) and abstract and single letter names (which they will use in their algebra work).

Understanding that a variable name represents a range of numbers. Algebra research has shown that pupils often do not understand that a variable name can represent a range of numbers. Discussion with the pupils about the meaning of a variable name in Logo elicits responses of the form 'the size of what it is going to be', ':SIDE stands for how far you want to get it to go', ':SCALE lets you know it can make it as big or as small as you want it'. They perceive the variable name as a 'place holder' for a general number. The pupils, however, seem to bring their earlier experiences of number in school mathematics to the Logo situation and the pupils' idea of 'range of numbers' was often restricted; for example, to positive integers. At least half of the case study pupils were initially resistant to using decimals in Logo. The 'Scaling Letter' task was valuable in provoking pupils to use decimals and through their engagement in this task they overcame this resistance. Six out of eight of the case study pupils carried the understanding that a variable name could represent a range of numbers from the Logo to the algebra context. The two pupils, Jude and Ravi, who did not respond positively, both had a very limited experience of variable in Logo. They also did not make any links between the Logo and algebra representations of function when carrying out the 'Function Machine' tasks.

Shahidur had some difficulty with the CSMS question, 'If John has J marbles and Peter has P marbles what could you write for the number of marbles they have altogether?' and his response indicates the transitional nature of his understanding. Writing down 9 as the solution, he gave the explanation:

Shahidur	"Cos John begins with J and there's four letters in John, and Peter begins with P and there's five letters in Peter.'
Researcher	'Why did you think P stands for 5?'
Shahidur	'Because I was wondering why they should put J and P.'
Researcher	'What if they were called Q and R?'

With this suggestion he immediately wrote down Q + R. Shahidur is not an algebra-experienced pupil and his mathematical attainment is very low. Under these circumstances his responses to the CSMS questions are quite extraordinary.

Table 12.2 Number of Sessions in which Variable has been used by the Case Study Pupils in their Logo Programming

CATEGORY OF USE	Pupil 1 SALLY	Pupil 2 ASIM	Pupil 3 GEORGE	Pupil 4 JANET	Pupil 5 JUDE	Pupil 6 RAVI	Pupil 7 LINDA	Pupil 8 SHAHIDUR
(I) One variable input	4	2	1	4	2	0	2	1
(S) Variable as scale factor	3	5	4	3	4	3	7	7
(N) More than one variable input	3	3	3	3	0	0	3	0
(O) Variable operated on	6	6	6	6	1	0	1	0
(G) General superprocedure	2	3	3	2	3	0	4	0
(R) Recursive procedure	2	3	3	2	0	0	0	0
(F) Input to mathematical function	2	2	2	4	1	2	3	2

Fig. 12.11 The 'Perimeter' Question (Küchemann, 1981)

Part of this figure is not
drawn. There are n sides
altogether all of them
length 2.

What is the perimeter of
this shape?

p = ...

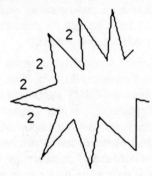

When presented with the perimeter question (Fig. 12.11) he wrote
down 2 x n's as a solution. When asked to explain his solution he
said, ''Cos there's the size of them are 2 ... and there are n's of
them ... so 2 times n will be the answer.'

*Understanding that different variable names can represent the same
value.* Another result from previous algebra research is that pupils
often do not understand that different variable names can represent
the same value. In order to test the longitudinal case study pupils'
understanding of whether or not a different variable name can
represent the same value, they were given the following Logo and
algebra questions (taken from CSMS (Küchemann, 1981)) (not
consecutively).

Fig 12.12 The 'Different Variable Names' Question

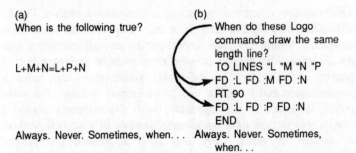

(a)
When is the following true?

L+M+N=L+P+N

Always. Never. Sometimes, when...

(b)
When do these Logo
commands draw the same
length line?
TO LINES "L "M "N "P
FD :L FD :M FD :N
RT 90
FD :L FD :P FD :N
END
Always. Never. Sometimes,
when. . .

Only Sally responded positively to both items but four out of eight
case study pupils responded positively to the Logo item. We

suggest that the pupils' Logo experience was sufficient for them to derive an understanding within a Logo context but was not yet extensive enough for them to use this understanding in a paper and pencil algebra context.

Ability to establish a second-order relationship between variable-dependent expressions. None of the case study pupils could answer either the CSMS algebra question, 'Which is the larger, 2n or n+2? Explain . . . ' or the Logo-related question correctly. Küchemann maintains that 'an important feature of these relationships is that their elements are themselves relationships, so they can be called "second order" relationships' (Küchemann, 1981). He maintains that it is only when pupils have grasped this notion that they have fully understood the idea of variable. None of the pupils had carried out any Logo tasks related to this idea. A further study has been undertaken with 10–11-year-old pupils in which they engaged in teacher-devised tasks specifically related to this idea. The results of this study show that if pupils use this idea during their 'hands-on' Logo work, then they are able to develop an understanding of the inter-relationship between two variable-dependent expressions (Sutherland, 1988).

Acceptance of 'lack of closure'. Previous studies have found that many pupils cannot accept that an unclosed algebraic expression is an algebraic object. So, for example, pupils are unable to accept that an expression of the form X + 3 could possibly be the solution of a problem. All of the case study pupils accepted lack of closure in a Logo expression. When compared with the comparison group more case study pupils than would have been expected accepted 'lack of closure' in the algebra context because of their experience of this type of expression in Logo.

Ability to use variable to represent a generalised method. Pupils' difficulties with algebra often arise from their informal methods in arithmetic. Within the Logo context pupils, through interacting with the computer, are able to develop their intuitive understanding of pattern and structure to the point where they can make a generalisation and formalise this generalisation in Logo. For some pupils in particular the interaction with the computer played a crucial role in their developing understanding of a general method. A session in which Sally and Janet negotiated the general relationship within a spiral is described in detail in Chapter 7.

IMPLICATIONS FOR CLASSROOM PRACTICE

In this chapter we have attempted to chart the development of algebraic ideas in a Logo environment and identify experiences which appear to have been significant for this development. We have also described some of the tasks and materials we have designed which either encourage the use of variable in Logo or build bridges between the Logo environment and the paper and pencil environment – in order that experiences in the former can serve as a conceptual framework for use in the latter.

We have classified the situations in which pupils can use variables to define general Logo procedures and these categories are useful as a basis for planning an appropriate range of activities for pupils. In particular we suggest that it is worthwhile distinguishing pupil activities which require an arithmetic understanding of variable (single variable or 'added-on' list of variables) from those which require more algebraic understanding (when operations are performed on a variable in order to construct another variable).

It is an important finding of the Logo Maths Project – as far as implications for classroom practice are concerned – that pupils rarely chose projects which 'needed' variable and they seemed to be resistant to the idea. The introduction of a task where variable input was used as a scale factor proved to be significant in this respect. We suggest that the idea of changing a fixed procedure to a general procedure by scaling distance commands is conceptually easier for pupils to use than making a general relationship explicit by operating on a variable input within a procedure. Pupils can play around with the idea of scaling figures. They can produce variable screen output, experience and appreciate the power of general procedures without necessarily being aware, at least at the initial stages, of all the characteristics of a general procedure and even exactly what is varying. However, with this introduction followed by more varied activities, pupils come to accept the idea of variable and become comfortable with the idea of a letter standing for a range of numbers – and this we feel is crucial.

Acceptance of a new idea is the only basis from which understanding can grow. We suggest that Logo experience can assist pupils in getting over this first hurdle and then can help build an understanding of the relationship between the signifier and signified in algebra, and in particular that the signifier, the variable name, is not significant in itself but only in terms of its relationship to other signifiers. We also found that pupils through interacting with the computer were able to develop their intuitive understanding of pattern and structure to the point where they could make a generalisation and formalise this generalisation in Logo. It is not easy to provide pupils with this type of experience in 'traditional' algebra. We suggest that Logo could be used as a context for generalising and formalising instead of attempting to contrive problems in 'beginning algebra'. We also have shown that with a certain level of experience of variable in Logo, pupils are able to use their developing understandings to solve problems in 'traditional' algebra.

Finally, it must be stressed again that all these benefits will not occur spontaneously. Teacher intervention is important in terms of monitoring the Logo activity in the context of pupils' own goals and in terms of the provision of structured tasks designed to provoke the use of variable in different ways. Games which motivate consideration of the process within a procedure are important here. It is also evident that pupils will not necessarily make the links between Logo and paper and pencil ideas. An important role for the teacher is to find ways to assist pupils in bringing their experiences together and surmounting contextual constraints. One way to do this, we suggest, is to devise bridging materials such as the function machine tasks in the Logo Maths Project in order to highlight the similarities and differences between variable in Logo and variable in algebra and to provide a forum for discussion of these issues.

ACKNOWLEDGEMENT

A modified version of this chapter has appeared in Sutherland, 1987.

13

Conclusions

The Logo Maths Project started at a time when computers were neither an accepted nor an established part of the mathematics curriculum. This situation is now changing rapidly and computers are now accepted within mathematics classrooms. If they are to become an established part of the curriculum it is important to continue to address the issues raised in this book, namely: the general impact of computer activity on mathematics learning; the variety of pupil approaches to Logo; the implications of discussion and collaboration between pupil pairs; gender differences; the use and developing understanding of mathematical ideas; and the role of the teacher.

1. Computer activity will have a general impact on the way mathematics is learnt in school. Pupils, by the time they have reached secondary school, have developed a dependence on the teacher as a provider of their mathematical knowledge. The computer can be a catalyst for challenging this dependence since, in an interactive environment, pupils can become involved in mathematical activity during which they pose their own problems, make their own decisions as to action and debug their representations on the basis of feedback. In the Logo Maths Project we found that it is possible to build up this pupil autonomy provided several conditions are met: pupils are initially allowed the freedom to devise their own goals; pupils have the opportunity to work in pairs at the computer; teacher interventions are process-directed rather than goal- directed and teacher interactions are aimed at both pushing the responsibility for decision making back to the pupils and provoking an awareness of concepts and relationships embedded within the computer activity. Within such a framework of teacher-pupil interaction we suggest that pupils are *necessarily* involved in

the problem-solving processes of conjecturing, testing out and debugging. Pupils will also become more systematic in the construction of their Logo procedures and develop debugging strategies in which programs with bugs are not quickly scrapped but are objects upon which to ponder.

We found that the opportunity afforded by the computer environment to change representation – between action-based, visual and symbolic – is significant to the success of the pupils' problem-solving activity. A change in representation, for example the creation of a written record whether spontaneous or suggested by a teacher, can frequently provoke a new perspective on a problem or a new way of coping with a bug. In particular we conjecture that the formalisation required by the programming language has an important influence on the problem- solving process. The requirement to program seems to 'force' pupils to reflect on their actions in direct mode and then 'capture' them in symbolic form. Thus the formalisation process can provide a 'bridge' between the pupils' actions and their generalisation – particularly if it is synthesised with graphical representation.

2. We identified a variety of pupil approaches to Logo programming – in terms of type of activity and in choice of goal. We also suggest that there are two major influences on pupils' use of structured programming design. The first influence is previous Logo activity – specifically experience of building up subprocedures into loosely-defined goals and defining superprocedures for the final image. The second influence arises from the nature and requirements of the pupil goals and the way these goals are perceived by the pupils. When pupils perceive their project to be one of working towards a real-world representation, the Logo commands are likely to become extensions of their drawing arm and subprocedures defined as a way of storing commands in a sequential manner. In such circumstances pupils do not perceive any need for their subprocedures to be reusable modules. They also think out their commands in a step-by-step linear way and debug similarly – that is with a local rather than global focus. In contrast, when pupils work on well-defined abstract goals, they are more likely to take a global perspective and plan their work in ways that more naturally suggest the idea of breaking a problem into parts and defining each part as a separate subprocedure. Pupils are also more likely to perceive modularity in cases where modules do not overlap, vary in size and are separated by an invariant sequence of 'navigating' commands. It is important therefore for a teacher to

design tasks where pupils will perceive the functionality and power of the idea of subprocedure.

3. Turning to the question of discussion and collaboration, there is no doubt that Logo programming provides an engaging problem-solving context. It was evident that not only are pupils provoked to talk – because of the public character of the screen and the immediate feedback afforded by the computer environment – but also that almost all of the talk tends to be task related. Despite marked variation between the patterns of interaction between pupil pairs, we suggest that collaborative exchanges can provide challenging ideas for projects; widen the range of projects chosen; keep a project going in the face of 'obstacles' and provoke appropriate changes in representation of the task; and facilitate the development of more flexible approaches to problem solving and programming. In addition, although initially the talk was action oriented, there was evidence of development towards more elaborated argument and explanation as the programming/mathematical issues became more complex.

Our research also identified individual conceptual development as a result of the three-way interaction between a pupil pair and the computer. In such cases the graphical feedback provided by the computer provoked reconsideration of ideas and also provided 'scaffolding' allowing a pupil to move on from an earlier conception. Such episodes also tended to provoke more supported argument between pupils – but this needs further investigation. We also suggest that collaborative work or discussion does not necessarily lead to individual learning gains in tightly specified circumstances. There are other influential factors – for example the nature of the task, the extent of explicit (or even implicit) agreement as to overall strategy or plan, and the social relations between the pupils. Also pupil pairs – particularly girls – tend to have implicitly negotiated individual dominance for particular aspects of any activity and this negotiation of dominance can impede individual acquisition of particular understandings.

4. Role demarcation is one of the gender differences identified in the Project. We also found that at the initial stages of the Logo work the boys tended to find it difficult to share interactions at the keyboard and within mixed sex pairs tended to dominate their partners. Although successful working partnerships eventually developed within the mixed sex pairs, it was noteworthy that no mixed pair 'survived' for the full three years of the project. We suggest that this phenomenon is a result of social influences

affecting relationships between boys and girls of ages around 13 to 14 years. Gender differences were also apparent arising, we suggest, from different expectations and subjective interpretations of the Logo activity. Girls, for example, are more likely to choose loosely-defined goals with an emphasis on the relationships between screen objects, while boys prefer more well-defined projects with an emphasis on the similarity of screen outcome to a preconceived design. We also observed differences in programming style between boys and girls. Girls seem to prefer a negotiating approach to programming in which individual modules are tried out in direct mode while boys tend to work in the editor and leave 'testing out' until a program is deemed to be finished. It is noteworthy that our evidence suggests that these differences in style do not reflect the presence or absence of any top-down plan or any differences in programming competence.

The nature of the discussion between pupil pairs also reflects gender differences. Girls are more likely to share with their partners their representations of the problem solution. They give more verbal support to their partner's suggestions and seek to develop an agreed plan of action. Boys in contrast tend to be more competitive in their verbal interactions and are more concerned to establish their autonomy, impose their problem representation on their partner or carry on working in their own way despite their partner's contributions! Boys can, however, learn to establish productive collaborative relationships and indeed take up each other's ideas – even if they do not like to acknowledge them explicitly! Our findings also indicate that boys tend to express a preference for working things out on their own and see arguments with peers as time consuming and diversionary. Girls, on the other hand, emphasise the importance of both the mutual help available within group work and the opportunity for the sharing of ideas.

5. Turning to a more mathematical focus, the Logo Maths Project raises issues concerning the use and developing understanding of mathematical ideas. We identified, for example, numerous instances when pupils used mathematics as a tool to achieve their programming goals. We also found that the mathematics used was not solely dependent on what was functional for a problem solution but also was affected by emotional resistance carried over from past mathematical experiences. In general terms our work highlights the extent of these emotional influences and how they frequently lead to restrictions in problem-solving activities. It also shows the fragmented way in which mathematical

knowledge tends to be constructed and how this knowledge is frequently inextricably intermeshed with contextual influences drawn from the settings in which it is used. The case studies also illustrate how the Logo environment with appropriate teacher intervention can go some way to overcome these fears and restrictions.

We suggest that insight into pupils' mathematical thinking gained through observation of their 'spontaneous' Logo programming can increase a teacher's awareness of pupil strategies and mathematical potential. The way mathematics is used provides an empirical window into pupils' conceptions of the mathematical ideas. We found that Logo programming not only illuminates pupil misconceptions but also can provide for the pupils a bridge to better understanding – through the cognitive conflict provoked by computer feedback, through the opportunity for experimentation with an idea leading to its acceptance and through the provision of an alternative, dynamic representation of mathematical concepts.

We gained insight into pupils' conceptions of a range of specific mathematical topics – such as decimals, ratio and proportion and variable. As far as variable is concerned, our research indicates that pupils do not necessarily see the need to use variable inputs to procedures and in the early stages of Logo work are not likely to choose projects which need this idea. Variable in Logo might best be introduced through tasks involving scaling since by this means pupils can explore and come to accept the power of a general procedure in a relatively undemanding context. Thus pupils can become comfortable with the idea that a letter can stand for a range of numbers and then, with a wider range of experience, can develop their intuitive understanding of pattern and structure to the point where they can make a generalisation and formalise this in a Logo program. It is not easy to provide pupils with this type of experience in 'traditional' algebra. We thus suggest that Logo can naturally and profitably be used as a context for generalising and formalising in place of the rather artificial problems often encountered in 'beginning algebra'. It is important to emphasise that these learning benefits do not occur spontaneously and teacher intervention is important in providing a symbolic form which matches the solution negotiated by the pupils in their interaction with the computer.

6. The final key issue concerns the role of the teacher. Our work highlights the crucial influence of intervention in the learning process and shows clearly that the presence of Logo does *not*

223

deprive teachers of responsibilities but rather presents new ways for thinking about the teaching/learning process. Firstly, there is a need for careful organisation of the Logo activities – for example teachers need to be aware that with scarce resources male pupils may try to dominate the hardware and strategies need to be devised to counteract this. Secondly, teachers should be aware that there are very different and equally effective ways of interacting with Logo and one way should not be allowed to take over. Pupils should be encouraged to develop flexibility in their approach to programming and in their choice of goals. Thirdly, teachers need to look out for possible pupil misconceptions about the nature of programming in Logo – concerning, for example, its sequential flow and the means by which control is passed from procedures to subprocedures. It is important that teachers are aware of these 'technical' obstacles and the possibility that the programming environment brings with it potential misconceptions as well as potential powers. We suggest that provoking a different form of representation of the programming mechanism (for example, the little people model, Harvey, 1985) could be a useful teaching strategy. Fourthly, pupil progress – or lack of progress – in certain areas is closely linked to the presence or absence of appropriate teacher intervention. We thus see a need both for pupils to work on teacher-devised tasks designed for specific learning outcomes and for teaching episodes in which the control of the interaction is more with the teacher than with the pupils. The balance between such teacher-initiated activities and pupil-directed exploration is, however, critical.

Teachers need to provoke pupils to predict and reflect and also open up new pathways to explore. Pupils do not automatically use knowledge constructed in one domain within another and understanding tends to be restricted to the context in which the knowledge was first appropriated. Teachers need to build connections between mathematical activities in Logo and non-Logo contexts and discuss similarities and differences in representations in the two settings. Thus, in summary the teacher is the pivotal mediator of the technicalities of the language, the mathematics embedded in the computer activity, the problem-solving processes and the connections between Logo and paper and pencil work.

To conclude, it is evident that Logo can provide a rich environment in which pupils can engage together in mathematical activity but the influence of the atmosphere in the mathematics classroom on pupil outcomes cannot be underestimated. The potential of computer environments such as Logo will only be realised if the pupils are able to work collaboratively with an emphasis on process rather than competitively with an emphasis on product. Pupils must be allowed the space to develop confidence to try things out for themselves in an experimental manner. We recognise that the development of such a mathematical environment is not straight-forward given the complexities of teaching and learning and the social relationships expected within school mathematics classrooms. We also know that Logo is not a trivial activity and needs a long time span and skilful teaching. We believe after our experience in the Logo Maths Project that the effort needed to incorporate Logo into mathematics classrooms will be worthwhile. We believe that the computer cannot change a poor learning environment into a good one but with open minds it can be a catalyst to question and reflect upon practice and learning.

We have learnt about pupils' mathematics by our observation of their Logo programming. We now know far more about how they think and feel about the subject. We also know more about our-selves as mathematics teachers. By analysing our interventions we have been able to reflect on our own preconceptions and biases. We have had experiences, too numerous to count, where we have laughed with pupils, argued with pupils and above all tried to learn from what they say and do. So we leave the last words to them:

'I think Lisa's sort of better [at maths] . . . you know, now that she sort of understands more with the computer . . . 'cos first of all when we first go on the computer she kept on going on about "I'm thick and everything" and now she doesn't say that any more . . . '

'I really like Logo and Maths – it's the only time that you work by yourself without the teacher telling you to stop what question you're on . . . ! We were making a super robot and we managed to get a moving picture. That was a good time because it took us ages and a lot of brain power.'

Appendix 1

Overview of Logo Commands

Throughout this study the pupils used RML Logo. This Logo does not possess infix operators (e.g. +, *). Instead the pupils had to use prefix operators (e.g. ADD, MUL).

The turtle starting position for this Logo is pointing horizontally to the right.

This RML version of Logo is no longer in common use and it has been decided to present the pupils' Logo procedures in a more standard form. However, it has been necessary to maintain the prefix operators. The following list of Logo commands contains those which have been used throughout this book:

FD n	Moves turtle forward n steps
BK n	Moves turtle backwards n steps
RT n	Turns turtle n degrees clockwise
LT n	Turns turtle n degrees anticlockwise
CS	Clears the graphics screen
CT	Centres the turtle
PU	Lifts the turtle pen
PD	Drops turtle pen
PE	Activates the turtle eraser
HT	Hides the turtle
ST	Shows the turtle
SETX n	Moves turtle horizontally to x-coordinate at n
SETY n	Moves turtle vertically to y-coordinate at n
SETXY n m	Moves turtle to x-coordinate at n and y-coordinate at m
SETH p	Sets the turtle heading to p degrees (0) vertically up the screen)

ARCL a b	Draws an arc to the left (radius a and size b (in degrees))
ARCR a b	Draws an arc to the right (radius a and size b (in degrees))
ADD p q	Outputs p added to q
SUB p q	Outputs q subtracted from p
MUL p q	Outputs p multiplied by q
DIV p q	Outputs p divided by q
GRQ p q	Tests to see if p is greater than q and outputs True or False
LRQ p q	Tests to see if p is less than q and outputs True or False
REPEAT n [abcd...]	This repeats the list of commands in the square brackets n times
TO name inputs	Signals start of title line of defined procedure
END	Indicates end of procedure definition
OUTPUT object	Returns control to calling procedure, with object as output.

Appendix 2

Categories of Pupil Discourse

CATEGORY 0

On task discourse which has nothing to do with the heuristic:
e.g. 'It's my turn to type now', 'Have you got a pencil?'

CATEGORY 1

Directions, prompts, suggestions, disagreements, propositions with no, or authoritarian support:

e.g. 'RT 45', 'It's 180, man, I'm telling you and I should know.'

Reaction to the screen with no explicit interpretation:

e.g. 'Yeh, that's about right.'

Simple answer to direct question:

e.g. Q 'How many FORWARD?'
    A '30.'

CATEGORY 2

Directions, prompts, suggestions, disagreements, propositions, explanations with support at a local level of action:

e.g. 'No, 'cos we done that 160.'

Reaction to screen explicitly using screen information for local support:

e.g. 'Look, we'll have to go back to the program. We probably forgot to put CENTRE.'

CATEGORY 3

Directions, prompts, suggestions, disagreements, propositions, explanations with reference to or indication of a global plan, or which refers to a general rule, theory or pattern:

e.g. 'Look, this is 5 and if we made it twice as big that's 10 and this is 6 and if this was twice as big it would be 12. Yeh, and if you said SUB JACK 10 that would give you 11 and that's too long for that.'

Extension of the task which takes into account the global overall structure of the whole project:

e.g. 'What you want is a program like this but instead of FD 10 you want to do the same for the angle so you can just put in a number and it will do it.'

CATEGORY Q

A question:

(a) Specifically requesting information:
    e.g. 'How far FORWARD?'
(b) Asking advice about a future plan or strategy:
    e.g. 'How would we do that?'
(c) Requesting an explanation:
    e.g. 'But how does it know what FORWARD is?'

References

Abelson, H. and DiSessa, A., (1981), *Turtle Geometry: The Computer as a Medium for Exploring Mathematics*, MIT Press, Cambridge, Mass.

Anderson, R.E., (1987), 'Females Surpass Males in Computer Problem Solving: Findings from the Minnesota Computer Literacy Assessment', *Journal of Educational Computing Research*, 3(1), 39–51.

APU Retrospective Report, (1985), *A Review of Performance in Mathematics 1978-1982*, HMSO, London.

Balacheff, N., (1984), 'French Research Activities in Didactics of Mathematics, some Key Words and Related References', *Theory of Mathematics Education*, Occasional Paper 54, Institut für Didaktich der Mathematik (IDM), Universität Bielefeld.

Balacheff, N., (1986), 'Construction and Observation of a Didactical Situation: The Sum of the Angles of a Triangle', *Proceedings of OBS1*, Nottingham University.

Bauersfeld, H., (1984), 'How to Develop Student/Pupil Investigations: Conditions and Strategies', Lecture presented at the Polytechnic of the South Bank, London.

Booth, L.R., (1984), *Algebra: Children's Strategies and Errors*, NFER-Nelson, Windsor.

Brown, M., (1981), *Place Value and Decimals*, in Hart, K. (ed.), *Children's Understanding of Mathematics: 11-16*, John Murray, London.

Brown, S.I. and Walter, M.I., (1983), *The Art of Problem Posing*, Lawrence Erlbaum Associates, Hillsdale, NJ.

Bruner, J., (1966), *Towards a Theory of Instruction*, Harvard University Press, Cambridge, Mass.

Byers, V. and Erlwanger, S., (1984), 'Content and Form in Mathematics', *Educational Studies in Mathematics*, 15, 259-75.

Carmichael, H., Burnett, J.D., Higginson, W.C., Moore, B.G. and Pollard, P.J., (1986), *Computers, Children and Classrooms: A Multisite Evaluation of the Creative Use of Microcomputers by Elementary School Children*, Queen's Printer for Ontario.

Clements, D.H., (1986), 'Logo and Cognition: A Theoretical Foundation', *Computers in Human Behavior*, 2, 95-110.

Cockcroft W.H., (1982), *Mathematics Counts*, HMSO, London.

DES, (1984), *Education Observed*, A review of published reports by HM Inspectors on primary schools and 11-16 and 12-16 comprehensive schools Department of Education and Science, Stanmore, Middx.

Dirckinck-Holmfeld, L., (1985), 'Information Technology and Cognitive Processes', *Proceedings of Third International GAST Conference*, London, April.

Fennema, E., (ed.), (1985), 'Explaining Sex-related Differences in Mathematics: Theoretical Models', *Educational Studies in Mathematics*, 16(3), 303–20.

Feurzig, W., Papert, S., Bloom, M., Grant, R. and Solomon, C., (1969), *Programming Languages as a Conceptual Framework for Teaching Mathematics*, Report 1889, Bolt Beranek & Newman, Cambridge, Mass.

Fife-Shaw, C., Breakwell, G.M., Lee, T., and Spencer, J., (1986), 'Patterns of Teenage Computer Usage', *Journal of Computer Assisted Learning*, 2, 152-61.

Gilligan, C., (1982), *In a Different Voice*, Harvard University Press, Cambridge, Mass.

Harper, E., (1987), 'Ghosts of Diophantus', *Educational Studies in Mathematics*, 18, 75-90.

Hart, K.M., (1981), *Children's Understanding of Mathematics 11-16*, John Murray, London.

Hart, K.M., (1984), *Ratio: Children's Strategies and Errors*, NFER-Nelson, Windsor.

Hartley, J.R., (1980), 'Using the Computer to Study and Assist the Learning of Mathematics', Occasional Paper No. 2, included in *Proceedings of BSPLM Conference*, Nottingham University, 3-4.

Harvey, B., (1985), *Computer Science Logo Style*, Vol. 1, MIT Press, Cambridge, Mass.

Hillel, J., (1985), 'On Logo Squares, Triangles and Houses', *For the Learning of Mathematics*, 5(2), 38–45.

Hillel, J., (ed.), (1987), *Proceedings of the Third Logo and Mathematics Education Conference*, Concordia University, Montreal.

Hillel, J., and Samurçay, R., (1985), *Analysis of a Logo Environment for Learning the Concept of Procedures with Variable*, Project Report, Concordia University, Montreal.

Hofstadter, D.R., (1985), *Metamagical Themes*, Bantam, New York.

Howe, J.A.M., O'Shea, T. and Plane, F., (1980), 'Teaching Mathematics through LOGO Programming: An evaluation study', in Tagg, E. and Lewis, R. (eds), *Computer Assisted Learning: Scope, Prospects and Limits*, North-Holland, Amsterdam.

Hoyles, C., (1985), *Culture and Computers in the Mathematics Classroom*, Bedford Way Paper, Institute of Education, University of London.

Hoyles, C., (1987), 'Tools for Learning: Insights for the Mathematics Educator from a Logo Programming Environment', *For the Learning of Mathematics*, 7(2), June, 32–7.

Hoyles, C. (ed.), (1988), *Girls and Computers: General Issues and Case Studies of Logo in the Mathematics Classroom*, Bedford Way Paper 34, Institute of Education, University of London.

Hoyles, C. and Noss, R. (eds), (1985), *Proceedings of the First Logo and*

Mathematics Education Conference, Institute of Education, University of London.

Hoyles, C., and Noss, R., (1987), 'Children Working in a Structured Logo Environment: From Doing to Understanding', *Recherche en Didactique de Mathématiques*, 8(1.2), 131–74.

Hoyles, C. and Noss, R., (1989), 'The Computer as a Catalyst in Children's Proportion Strategies', *Journal of Mathematical Behaviour*, 8, 53–75.

Hoyles, C., Noss, R. and Sutherland, R. (eds), (1986), *Proceedings of the Second Logo and Mathematics Education Conference*, Institute of Education, University of London.

Kieran, C., (1985), 'The Evolution of Geometric Thinking Among 10 and 11 year olds using Logo', *Proceedings of the Second Logo and Mathematics Education Conference*, Institute of Education, University of London.

Kilpatrick, J., (1985), 'A Retrospective Account of the Past Twenty-five Years of Research on Teaching Mathematical Problem Solving', in Silver, E. (ed)., *Teaching and Learning Mathematical Problem Solving: Multiple Research Perspectives*, Lawrence Erlbaum Associates, Hillsdale, NJ, 1–15.

Küchemann, D., (1981), 'Algebra', in Hart, K. (ed.), *Children's Understanding of Mathematics: 11-16*, John Murray, London.

Lave, J., Murtaugh, M. and de la Roche, O., (1984), 'The Dialectics of Arithmetic in Grocery Shopping', in Rogoff, B. and Lave, J. (eds), *Everyday Cognition*, Harvard University Press, Cambridge, Mass., 67–95.

Leron, U., (1983), 'Some Problems in Children Learning LOGO', *Proceedings of the Seventh Conference for the Psychology of Mathematics Education*, Israel.

Leron, V., (1985), Logo Today: Reason and Reality, *The Computing Teacher*, 12, 5, February, 26–32.

Lockheed, M.E., (1985), 'Women, Girls and Computers: A First Look at the Evidence', *Sex Roles*, 13, (3/4).

Mandl, H., De Corte, E., Bennett, N. and Friedrich, H.F. (eds), (1988), *Learning and Instruction in an International Context*, Vols II and III, Pergamon, Oxford.

Mason, J., Burton, L. and Stacey, K., (1982), *Thinking Mathematically*, Addison-Wesley, London.

Minksy, M., (1986), *The Society of Mind*, Simon & Schuster, New York.

Moore, B., (1986), *Equity in Education: Gender Issues in the Use of Computers. A Review and Bibliography*, Review and Evaluation Bulletins, Ministry of Education, Ontario, 6(1).

Nielsen, J., (1987), "This is a Very Predictable Machine" – said Michael – on Computers on Human Cognition', in Gregory, R., (ed.), *Creative Intelligence*, Pinter, London.

Nielsen, J., and Roepstorff, L., (1985), 'Girls and Computers – Delight or Necessity', *Proceedings of the Third GASAT Conference*, London.

Noss, R., (1985), *Creating a Mathematical Environment through Programming: A Study of Young Children Learning Logo*, Institute of Education, University of London.

Noss, R., (1986), 'Constructing a Conceptual Framework for Elementary

Algebra through Logo Programming', *Educational Studies in Mathematics*, 17(4), 335–57.

Noss, R., Smallman, C. and Thorne, M., (1985), *Microworlds: Adventures with Logo*, Hutchinson, London.

Papert, S., (1980), *Mindstorms: Children, Computers, and Powerful Ideas*, Basic Books, New York.

Papert, S., (1986), 'Beyond the Cognitive. The Other Face of Mathematics', Lecture Notes. *Proceedings of the Tenth International Conference of the Psychology of Mathematics Education*, Plenary Lectures, London.

Papert, S., Watt, D., diSessa, A. and Weir, S. (1979), *Final Report of the Brookline Logo Project*, Logo Memos 53 and 54, Massachusetts Institute of Technology, Cambridge, Mass.

Pea, R.D. and Kurland, D.M., (1984), 'On the Cognitive Effects of Learning Computer Programming', *New Ideas in Psychology*, 2(2), 137–68.

Polya, G., (1945), *How to Solve It*, Princeton University Press, Princeton, NJ.

Rouchier, A. and Samurçay, R., (1985), 'Didactical Studies of Teaching Situations. What About Logo?', *Proceedings of the First Logo and Mathematics Education Conference*, Institute of Education, University of London.

Schoenfeld, A.H., (1985), 'Metacognitive and Epistemological Issues in Mathematical Understanding', in Silver, E. (ed.), *Teaching and Learning Mathematical Problem Solving, Multiple Research Perspectives*, Lawrence Erlbaum Associates, New Jersey, 361–80.

Sutherland, R., (1987), 'What are the links between variable in Logo and Variable in algebra?', *Recherches en Didactique des Mathématiques*, 8(1-2), 103–30.

Sutherland, R., (1988), 'A Longitudinal Study of the Development of Pupils' Algebraic Thinking in a Logo Environment', PhD thesis, Institute of Education, University of London.

Tourniaire, F. and Pulos, S., (1985), 'Proportional Reasoning: A Review of the Literature', *Educational Studies in Mathematics*, 16, 181-204.

Turkle, S., (1984), *The Second Self, Computers and the Human Spirit*, Simon and Schuster, New York.

Vergnaud, G., (1982), 'Cognitive and Developmental Psychology and Research in Mathematics Education: Some Theoretical and Methodological Issues', *For the Learning of Mathematics*, 3(2), 31–41.

Vygotsky, L., (1978), *Mind in Society*, Harvard University Press, Cambridge, Mass.

Wagner, S., (1981), 'Conversation of Equation and Function under Transformations of Variable', *Journal for Research in Mathematics Education*, 12(2), 107-18.

Weir, S., (1987), *Cultivating Minds: A Logo Casebook*, Harper & Row, New York.

Wood, D., Bruner, J. and Ross, G., (1976), 'The Role of Tutoring in Problem Solving', *Journal of Child Psychology and Psychiatry*, 17, 89-100.

Index

Abelson, H. 6
abstract goals: choice of 146;
    well-defined 77
activity: exploratory 59;
    goal-directed 60–4; interactive 58
algebra 194–218; closure in 216;
    function and Logo 203–9;
    implications for classroom
    practice 217–20; variable
    195–203, 209–16 *see also*
    mathematics
Anderson, R.E. 163
angle, concept of 116–17
Artificial Intelligence Laboratory
    (MIT) 5
Assessment of Performance Unit
    (APU) 116, 117, 184

Balacheff, N. 117, 178
Bauersfeld, H. 179
Booth, L.R. 178, 194
'bottom up' programming 66; and
    gender 167; and sub-procedures
    71–2
Breakwell, G.M. 161
Brookline Logo Project 8
Brown, M. 184
Brown, S. 57
Bruner, J. 55, 98
Burton, L. 55
Byers, V. 194

Carmichael, H. 160–1, 162–3, 165–6
case studies: interview with pupils
    135–7; overview 80; and variables

214 *see also* projects; tasks
classroom climate 56
classroom practice: and algebra
    217–20; and collaborative work
    114–15; and computers 2; and
    gender 176–7; in mathematics
    192–3; and problem solving 69;
    and pupil's misconceptions 96;
    sub-procedures 86–8; teachers'
    role 157–8; on turtle turn and
    angle 137–9
Clements, D.H. 58
Cockroft, W.H. 55, 97, 140
collaboration 97–115; examples of
    100–7; exchanges 99–100; and
    gender 171–5; implications for
    classroom practice 114–15; and
    individual work 108–14; and
    problem solving 221; response
    111–14; utterances, coding of
    107–8 *see also* pupil pairs
computers 1–2; in classrooms 2; and
    functions in algebra 205–6; and
    gender 159–60; impact of 219–20;
    implications for classroom
    practice 2; interactions with
    165–71; interactive activity with
    58; and mathematics 219
control: confusion over mode in
    Logo 89–90; direct 89–90, 93;
    flow of 94–5

debugging 58, 67, 90–1; in Logo 7;
    'M' task 128–31
decimals: concept of 184–9;

confusion over 187–9; ordering, incorrect 187; resistance to using 185–6
Department of Education and Science (DES) 97
deSessa, A. 6
dimensions: of goals in turtle graphics 61–4, 72–7; of programming style 65–6
Dirckinck-Holmfeld, L. 162
discourse, pupils *see* pupil discourse
Education Observed (DES) 97
Erlwanger, S. 194
extended study 9, 14–15; and gender 166

Fennema, E. 164
Feurzig, W. 5, 7, 8
Fife-Shaw, C. 161
filenames 90
framework, conceptual for ideas 153–4
Function Machine 200; paper & pencil tasks 208; as task 205–6
functions in algebra: aims of Logo and 204–5; computer-based activity 205–6; and Logo 203–9; paper & pencil tasks 207–9; pupils' learning of 207–9; representation of 203–4

gender 159–77; approach to problems 167–9; assumptions 159–60; attitude to mode of working 175–6; collaboration of pupils pairs 171–5; differences in approach 221–2; implications for classroom practice 176–7; interaction with computer 165–71; and Logo Maths Project 164; and programming 161–4; of pupils pairs 11; role demarcation 221–2; and variable names 169–71
Gilligan, C. 163
girls *see* gender
goal-directed activity: choice of 64; classification of 63; defined 62; dimensions of 61–4; programming 60–4

goals: building new 32–3; choice of 146; dimensions of 61–4; extending 28–30; gender 165; structured, in programming 72–8 *see also* goal-direction activity; loosely-defined; real world
group learning: turtle turn and angle 116–39

Harper, E. 194, 195
Hart, K. 189
Hartley, J.R. 8
Harvey, B. 71, 72, 96
heuristic processes 55, 57–8
Hillel, J. 71–2, 117, 149, 195
Hofstadter, D.R. 160
Howe, J.A.M. 8
Hoyles, C. 98, 189

individual work 109–11
interactive activity 5; with computers 58
intervention: categories of 142–3; ideas in projects 30–2; and pupils' control 143–5; and teacher-devised tasks 145–54; by teachers 42–6; teaching episodes 154–6; ways of 141–3
interview: with pupils on case studies 135–7; on variable in algebra 211, 214

Kieran, C. 117
Kilpatrick, J. 55–6
knowledge: base 56–7; fragmented domain of 179–82
Kücherman, D. 194, 215, 216
Kurland, D.M. 8, 58

Lave, J. 56–7
learning: contextual influences 182–3; fragmented domain of 179–82; restricted environment 183–4
Lee, T. 161
Leron, U. 8, 71, 141, 149
LISP 5
lists, in Logo 6

Lockheed, M.E. 161
Logo: algebraic functions 204–5; commands, overview of 226–7; debugging 7; interaction 7; links to algebra 203–9; and mathematics 7–9; primitives 5; and problem solving 57–8; procedures 5, 6, 7; programming activity 5–7; programming and gender 161–4; pupil approaches to 220–1; recursion 7; structured programming 71–8; syntactical level 59; variable, concept of 195–203, 209–16
Logo Maths Project 5–15; aims 3–4, 55, 98; analysis of 14; case studies 10–13; in classroom 224–5; concept of turn and angle 117–18; data collection 13; design of 9–10; extended study 14–15; and gender 164; issues 4; Longitudinal Study 3; mathematics 219; pupil autonomy 219–20
Longitudinal Case Study: analysis of data 14; case studies 16–54; intervention strategies 141–3; Logo commands 226–7; pupils' solutions 212; research 9–11
loosely-defined goals: cognitive demands 197; and gender 165–6; in problem solving 61–4; in structured programming 72–6; teacher's role 146

Mason, J. 55
mathematics: changes in teaching 97–8; conceptual framework 153–4; decimals 184–9; ideas, use of 151–3; implications for classroom practice 192–3; insight into ideas 222–3; intuitive concepts 178–93; learning 7–9, 179–84; and Logo Maths Project 2, 219; problem solving 55–7; ration and proportion 189–92; and role of teacher 140–58 see also algebra
Mathematics in the National

Curriculum (DES) 2
metacognition 56
Minsky, M. 57
misconceptions of pupils: control of flow 94–5; debugging 90–1; file name 90; implications for classroom practice 96; mode in Logo 89–90; procedures 90; repeated structures 91–2; sub-procedures 92–4
mode in Logo, confusion over 89–90
modularity 24, 71; pupils' development and 79–84; teacher-devised tasks 77–8
Moore, B. 161

National Curriculum for Mathematics 2
Nielson, J. 163, 174–5
Noss, R. 57, 98, 189, 195

paper & pencil tasks: Function Machine 208; functions in algebra 207–9; and gender 166
Papert, S. 5, 7, 8, 117, 163
Pea, R.D. 8, 58
Plane, F. 8
planning, and program style 66
Polya, G. 55
primitives 5 see also Logo: commands
problem solving 55–69; and collaboration 221; development of 221; and gender 167–9; goals 64; implications for classwork practice 69; and Logo 57–8; and mathematics 55–7; programming 59–63, 65–9; synthesis 69
procedures 5, 6, 7; defining 21; implications for classwork practice 86–8; modularity 70–2, 79–84; names 90; phases writing in 85–6; recursion in 203; state-transparent 18; structures 83–4; and sub-procedures 70–88, 92–4, 203; superprocedure 203; variable input 201–2 see also projects; tasks

programming: case studies 60–1, 67–9; debugging 67; early attempts at 150–1; exploratory 59; and gender 161–4; goal-directed 60–4; language 220–1; in Logo 5–7; modules 70–2, 79–84; planning 66–7; pupils, confronting with ideas 146–51; pupils' misconceptions 89–96; structured 72–8; style 65–9; and sub-procedure 70–2; syntactical level 59; types 59–63 *see also* bottom up; top-down

programming environment, collaboration 97–115

projects: Aeroplane 41–7; BFLY 67–8; Butterfly 60; Cube 33–9; Face 121–2; Goal Post 127–8; House 74; MAD 73–4; part of a spiral 102–6; Plane 39–47; Prison 61; Rabbit 76; Rotated Patterns 181; selected 16–54; Spiral 24–33; Star 77; STARBUSTER 16–24, 61–2; Turtle 123–7; Variable Star 187; Whizzy Effects 47–54 *see also* tasks

proportion *see* ratio

Pulos, S. 189

pupil development: modularity, use of 79–84; phases in 85–6; sub-procedures, using 79–84

pupil discourse, categories of 228–9

pupil pairs: aims of project 98; and algebraic functions 207–9; autonomy 219–20; chosen 10–11; collaboration 97–115; and concept of turn and angle 118–28; control, encouraging 143–5; exchanges 99–100; gender, collaboration 171–5; gender of 11; and goals 99; and individual work 108–14; structured tasks 128–35; utterances 107–8; working 12–13 *see also* case studies

pupils: contextual influences on concepts 182–3; control, developing 143–5; decimals, concept of 184–9; goals, changing 146; interview with 135–7; intuitive mathematics in 178–93; learning mathematics 179–84; misconceptions *see* misconceptions of pupils; and programming 146–51; ratio and proportion, concept of 189–92; restricted learning environment 183–4; variable, concept of 197

ratio and proportion 189–92

real world goals; choice of 146; in problem solving 61–4; in structured programming 72–6

recursion 7; procedures in algebra 203; unplanned 93–4

repeated structures 91–2

research: design 9–10; extended study 9; Longitudinal Case Study 9–11; team 12 *see also* pupil pairs

Roepstorf, L. 174–5

Ross, G. 98

Rouchier, A. 147

Samurçay, R. 71–2, 147, 195

scale/scaling 185–9, 197–201

Schoenfeld, A.H. 56

School Mathematics Individualised Learning Experience (SMILE) 10, 15

School Mathematics Project (SMP) 13, 15

Spencer, J. 161

Stacey, K. 55

structured programming, influences on 220–1

structured tasks: responses 130–5; results 128–35

sub-procedure *see* procedure

superprocedure 203

Sutherland, R. 216, 218

tasks: Arrow 111–14, 169–74, 190–2; Box 92–3; Decreasing Squares 82, 95, 168, 210, 212; Different Variable Name 215; Four Squares 79–84, 91–5; function machine 205–6; and gender 166–8; 'K' 166–7; lollipop 109–11, 212; 'M' debugging 128–31, 166–7; paper & pencil function machine 208; Pat tracing 133; Perimeter Question 215; Puzzle 132; Regular Polygon 152; REPEAT 134; Rotated Patterns 180–1; Row of Pines 78, 155–6, 186; Scaling Letter 185–9, 197–201, 213; SMILE 147–8; and solutions 212; Variable Squares 149, 212 *see also* projects

teacher/teaching: -devised tasks 145–54; episodes 154–6; implications for classroom practice 157–8; and modularity 79–84; role of 140–58, 223–4

'top-down' design 66; and gender 167; and sub-procedures 70–1

Tourniare, F. 189

Turkle, S. 162, 183

turn *see* angle

turtle: goals, dimensions of 61–4; and graphics 5–6, 7; implications for classroom practice 137–9; turn and angle 116–39

variable in algebra 24; acceptance of idea of 211; categories of 201–3; concept of 195–203; different names for 215; gender and names 169–71; generalised methods 216; individual laboratory tasks 210; as input 201–2; name, understanding 211–13; number range of 213–15; pupils' understanding of 209–16; structured interview 211, 214

Vergnaud, G. 196

video recordings 13–14

Vygotsky, L. 98, 145

Walter, K.I. 57

Weir, S. 140–1

well-defined goals: abstract 77; and gender 165–6, 167; in problem solving 61–4; in structured programming 72–6; teacher's role 146

Wood, D. 98